12. NOV. 1966

AUTHOR
REDGRAVE P.

CLASS No.
F.

TITLE
Full fathom

six

BOOK No.
8363576.

This book m...   ...above

FULL FATHOM SIX

When Henry Warren, a young Oxford graduate, joined the Royal Navy and then volunteered for service as a gunner on merchant ships, he did not expect to find himself solely in charge of his first ship's armaments—particularly as he had never fired anything bigger than a Lewis gun while training. However, through an error, such was his predicament. This story tells how he resolved it, and many others, on his voyages during the early years of the Second World War.

The scenes shift from the ocean terrors of the North Atlantic to the peaceful prosperity of the United States before their entry into the war; then down to the tropical seas and the west coast of Africa. The tale is told swiftly and is packed with action, dry humour and shrewd observation of people and places. The author, a poet who lives on the edge of Dartmoor, was himself a naval gunlayer on merchant ships during the years 1941 to 1944.

FULL FATHOM SIX

by

PAUL REDGRAVE

ROBERT HALE LIMITED
63 Old Brompton Road London S.W.7

Set and printed by
Clarke, Doble & Brendon, Ltd., Oakfield Press, Plymouth
in ten point Baskerville

PART ONE

I

In January, 1941, the Royal Navy sent me to Liverpool to join my first merchant ship as an able seaman-gunner.

Snow fell softly as the navy-blue lorry dumped me and my hammock and two kit-bags alongside the towering bows of the s.s. *Vesta*.

"There she is, mate. All yours," said the hearty driver.

"Thanks very much, but how am I supposed to get aboard?" I answered. The driver pointed to a gangway near the vessel's stern. It sloped upwards at a perilous angle.

"Up the plank," he suggested, then drove off with an easy, insolent skill.

I was about to ask myself why he hadn't backed up nearer to the "plank" when I noticed that by the foot of the gangway a large black van was parked. It said POLICE above the windscreen. The back doors were wide open and a lipless policeman sat at the driving wheel. I nodded to him as I passed with my hammock, but he still sat as though made of Black Maria, so I propped my hammock against a bollard and went to fetch the rest of my gear. As I returned, dragging the two kit-bags, a large policeman loomed at the head of the gangway. He began to descend, followed by a stocky, red-bearded seaman who appeared to be handcuffed. He was being steadied from behind by yet another large policeman. The gangway winced and bent as they neared the middle. I watched fearfully, then sighed with relief as it resumed its normal shape when they neared the bottom. The seaman noticed me. He grinned and flashed piratical teeth:

"Joinin' this hooker?"

I nodded. The man let out a great roar of red-bearded laughter.

"Poor sucker!"

I think he said "sucker." Anyway, with the north-country accent he used the word rhymed with "hooker."

"That's enough o' that," said the policeman behind him. "You've got enough charges to answer to without adding one of 'using obscene language'."

Redbeard's reply to his escort was highly entertaining, but

unprintable. The policemen bundled him into the van, climbed in themselves and shut the doors. As they drove away I could hear thuds and bangs as though the prisoner were trying to kick his way to freedom.

Mentally shrugging off the affair as no business of mine, I started up the gangway with my hammock, leaving the kit-bags on the quay. No one was on deck so I dumped the hammock and brought up my bags, one at a time. After the third ascent I sat down breathlessly on a bag and looked around me. My pith helmet looked oddly out of place tied to the neck of the other bag and lying on its side in the thin layer of snow which covered the deck, the strewn ropes and assorted gear scattered about. Perhaps it will come in handy, I thought hopelessly, staring at the topee.

I knew a little about ships, not much, but enough to realise that the s.s. *Vesta* was a tanker. Her funnel was set right aft and a long fore and aft or flying-bridge spanned the deck distance from the after-accommodation to amidships, and from there to the fo'c'sle. There was a light in what seemed to be the saloon, for though it was morning the sky was dark with falling snow. Disliking the idea of approaching the saloon first, I began to pick my way further towards the stern, uncertain whether the crew, or the "crowd"—as they say on merchant ships—would be quartered there or in the forward part of the ship. It was very slippery and I hadn't gone far when my foot caught in a snow-covered coil of rope and down I crashed, full length on the iron deck! The noise must have had some effect for as I got up and began to knock the snow off my coat, a frightened face appeared at the open door of a nearby booby-hatch, and a hunch-backed figure half emerged. I glared at the startled eyes and put on a tough accent:

"Where's the chief officer, mac?"

The youth babbled something in Clydeside Scotch which was quite unintelligible to me, then he turned and bolted back down his hole. I decided to brave the saloon at once.

There was no one in it, so I knocked on the first cabin door starboard side, that I came to.

"Come in!"

I entered and a one-ringed officer stood up to meet me. He had a big, pleasant face with thick, black eyebrows which curled upwards, giving him an inquisitive and slightly Mephistophelean expression. Under his uniform jacket he wore a white, roll-neck sweater.

"What can I do for you?" he asked.

"I'm looking for the chief officer. Can you direct me to him?"

The officer laughed.

"Even if I could, I wouldn't. We haven't seen him for days. He's probably somewhere you're too young to go."

Because I was young, I resented the last remark, but said nothing.

"Are you the new DEMS bloke?" the officer asked, suddenly serious.

DEMS. Or more properly, D.E.M.S. Or if you really had time to spare, "Defensively Equipped Merchant Ships." This was the ponderous title of a branch of Royal Navy gunners of which I was a new, voluntary member. I had taken a gunnery course in Devonport Barracks which lasted four weeks and had qualified as a seaman-gunner without actually firing anything bigger or noiser than a Lewis. After three months at sea I could take another month's course and become a gunlayer. This meant taking full charge of a gun and crew of seven or nine merchant seamen. A seaman-gunner was simply a gunlayer's assistant. He trained the gun on the target while the layer elevated, depressed and fired the gun, and of course, gave all the orders.

"Yes," I admitted, "I'm the new DEMS bloke."

"Gunlayer?"

"Seaman-gunner."

He then asked the dreaded question:

"Been to sea before?"

"I went to France once—before the war."

"Christ! Well, sit down somewhere. Like a drink?"

"Yes please—sir," I answered gratefully, remembering that perhaps I should have said "sir" when I first addressed him. He read the thought.

"Don't 'sir' me," he said, "we don't go for that Navy stuff in the Merchant Service. And no saluting either—except the captain—if you want to. I'll take you to see him in a minute, when he gets his wind back."

I must have looked puzzled, for he continued:

"Had a spot o' bother with one of the men just before you arrived. Mutinous bastard!"

The third officer—as I had now realized he was—took a quick gulp at his neat whisky. I sipped the one he had handed me and enjoyed the sensation of warm, minor explosions which seemed to be occurring in my stomach. I had never drunk anything stronger than the Royal Navy's "two and one" (two parts water, one part rum) issued in shore bases. I ventured to ask about Redbeard:

"What had he done?"

The third snorted.

"What had he not!"

He took another quick gulp.

"To mention a few things, he tried to jump ship at every port we called at last trip, smuggled a woman aboard at Halifax, flogged ship's gear at St. John's, slashed one of the greasers with a cut-throat razor, tried to bribe a customs bloke—an honest one —pinched the chief steward's pocket watch, filled in the sparker, and about an hour ago we caught him in the act of trying to sabotage the ship's engines. He resisted arrest, so the police put the shackles on him!"

"Are there any more like him, still at large?" I asked.

The third officer laughed.

"Oh, no, we're all pretty normal," he said.

I thought of the incoherent, deformed youth who had scuttled off down the hatch; I thought of the absent mate; I wondered.

"He was a Liverpool-Irishman," the third went on, as if this explained everything, "Proper bastard!"

He tossed off the rest of his whisky, stood up and buttoned his coat, then said:

"Well, now for the Old Man."

I tried to gulp down the last finger of whisky in my glass in imitation, but nearly choked. The third laughed and slapped me on the back.

"You need practice," he said. "By the way, what's your name?"

"Warren," I coughed, "Henry Warren."

"And I'm Michael O'Neil—and I'm not entirely at your service," the third chuckled.

"Irish?"

We stepped out into the passage-way, into a cold, cutting wind.

"Liverpool-Irish," said the voice full of brogue, charm, blarney and leprechauns.

Third Officer Michael O'Neil led me up a ladder to the 'midships boat-deck where the captain had his accommodation, immediately below the chart-room and wheel-house. I caught a glimpse of my kit-bags far below on the deck. Someone had stood them up and they looked like two short snowmen, one wearing a topee. The third mate knocked on the door of the captain's cabin. A high, stridulous voice piped:

"Come in!"

The cabin was spacious and, for a cargo ship, luxuriously furnished. My feet sank into a thick, fitted carpet and I waded through it towards the desk where Captain Eldrich was sitting. He was a small man with the face of a pensive elf. He looked thoughtfully at me when I handed him my paper from the

DEMS office, telling who and what I was. I was standing stiffly to attention, a habit formed by five months' naval discipline.

"Don't be so tense," the captain cried suddenly, his voice crackling like fire in dry grass. "It affects my nerves."

He dismissed the third officer with a nod and I relaxed slightly while he read the note, then flipped it amongst a pile of ship's papers and correspondence which lay scattered on the desk. He swivelled round in his chair, clasped his hands tightly and began to twiddle his tiny thumbs, first this way, then that. He raised the remnants of his eyebrows in my direction and drew a sharp breath, like a whistle turned inside out.

"First ship?" he exhaled.

Alarmed, I wondered how on earth he knew. It didn't say on the paper that the s.s. *Vesta* was to be my first ship. The third hadn't told him. Was I so lettuce-green to look at, then, or was the captain really shrewd? I gave myself up without a fight.

"Yes, sir," I meekly answered.

The captain's thumb-twiddling ceased. He picked up a pencil and studied its broken point, then he suddenly threw it on the desk.

"School?" he shot at me.

I told him.

"And after that?"

"Oxford."

"Ah!"

He picked up the pencil and gave it more sedulous attention. "It's a wonder," he pondered, "It's a wonder they didn't commission you."

This sort of remark was not new to me. For the past three months I'd heard it from my father—by letter of course, from other ratings and from the one W.R.N.S. officer I'd chanced to meet who had found it socially difficult to have anything to do with me. Moreover, she suspected that even trying to was an infringement of some Admiralty Fleet Order, hence the affair was short-lived. There was no definite reason why I hadn't been commissioned, none that I knew of, that is—and as the captain's last remark could be taken either as a rhetorical question or a plain statement, I didn't venture to answer him.

He let it go at that, dismissing me with a curt nod. I went straight down to the third's cabin and asked him where I was supposed to sleep and eat. He told me that I was to share a two-berthed cabin aft with the gunlayer, when he arrived. The gunner's accommodation was with the engineer officers. At sea we dined in their mess-room, but in port we all sat at the captain's table in the saloon, because it was more convenient for some reason.

"Lunch," said the third, "will be in half an hour, so if you get your gear together the engineers' mess-boy will show you where to stow it."

I thanked him and proceeded aft, dragging my bags over the slippery deck and finally dropping them into some dark depths at the bottom of a ladder on the port side. They nearly landed on the head of the mess-boy—none other than the limping hunchback—who gave a yell and started back into his pantry, from which he had just been in the act of emerging. He turned out to be friendly, but garrulous and gossipy. After a while I found his barbarous accent fairly understandable and we got on very well. He told me his name was Colin and showed me to the gunners' cabin which was directly under the poop. On the deck overhead was a rudder-chain of Promethean size which would rattle like thunder once we got to sea. I would get used to it, Colin assured me. The bulkhead on one side of the cabin curved upwards, following the shape of the stern and port quarter of the vessel. There was a wash-basin about the size of those in use on trains, with a bucket for drainage underneath and a cracked mirror above. A large set of drawers took up too much space in the cabin, but would be more civilized than kit-bags, I decided. There were two bunks, an upper and a lower. After some deliberation I chose the upper, just in case the gunlayer turned out to be a heavy drinker who might use my face as a mounting stool when clambering into his bunk after a night ashore. I hoped that when he arrived he wouldn't claim it for himself, having perhaps similar ideas about me.

Colin offered to do my washing for a consideration; but I told him I could manage my own dobhying. One couldn't afford service on three-and-sixpence a day, plus the sixpence a day I should get from the ship's owners. This sixpence was a token payment for being signed on the articles as a deck-hand. Sailing thus under false colours was a precaution in case a gunner fell into enemy hands, for it was hoped that he might pass as a merchant seaman. He would then have civilian status which meant internment instead of imprisonment for the duration of the war, though as far as treatment was concerned, the distinction between an internee and a prisoner of war in Germany seemed an academic one.

There were other, more colourful stories connected with the fact that DEMS ratings carried civilian clothes amongst their kit. One was that if we stepped ashore at a neutral port wearing uniform we should immediately be arrested and interned as "members of a belligerent nation." Another was that if we were seen in one of these ports by enemy agents they might have us kidnapped and tortured or bribed—but mostly tortured—for information. A third barrack story chronicled us as Churchill's Spies, a title given to us, it was said, by Lord Haw-Haw in one of his vitriolic speeches, and as such we were condemned to death should we be captured by Germans or Italians (the Japs not yet being in the war). This last story I enjoyed best of all and retold it to so many laymen that I began to believe it myself and felt quite scared, but brave.

I had gained a remarkable sense of freedom now that I had actually joined a ship as a DEMS gunner. Royal Naval discipline had little appeal for me. I believed that the only worthwhile discipline was self-discipline which brings with it a sense of personal triumph. Orders from outside which crushed people into a pattern, gave them numbers, called them "ratings," unnerved and appalled me however necessary it all was.

Colin's brown, cow-eyes boggled when he saw the contents of my first kit-bag which I emptied on to the deck of the cabin. It contained both tropical and arctic kit—besides my civilian suit. In DEMS one had to be prepared to journey without warning to any point of the compass. I hurriedly stuffed most of the things into drawers and hung my duffle coat on a nail beside the bunks. My seaboots were stowed at the bottom of the other bag and I'd decided to wear them because of the snow. After lugging them to the surface I'd just started to put them on when Colin noticed their newness. He put his head on one side, like a dog.

"It's no yer first ship, is it?" he asked suspiciously.

I inwardly cursed him for his shrewdness and myself for allowing him to see the boots before I'd had the chance of dirtying them. Although I apparently couldn't fool the captain I hoped that the crew wouldn't find out at once that I was a "first tripper," mainly for the sake of the discipline and morale of the gun's crew. I doubted if I should be able to fool all the ship's people all of the time, but I was determined to try. Here was the first test.

"It's no yer first ship, is it?" Colin repeated, anxiously this time. He apparently put a lot of trust in the ship's gunners.

"First merchant packet," I answered, in what I thought to be a very tough, laconic manner.

The mess-boy looked immensely relieved. I was not a green gunner after all.

"Was youse aboard a battleship?" he cried excitedly.

I casually flung a bit of naval jargon about.

"No battlewagons for me, mate. Too pusser."

Colin looked impressed.

"A destroyer then?"

"Yes, please," I said.

I'd once asked a matelot in barracks if he was on a destroyer and he had said "Yes, please." Also I'd been aboard one of the ex-American Lease-Lend destroyers and remembered the name of it in case Colin asked me.

"One o' the ex-Yankee boats," I added casually. "They roll like logs. Lost all my gear on her when she got the hammer. Had to get some new."

Hence the new seaboots. Colin bought the lot and would obviously spread it around the ship that I was a real Navy gunner with survivor's gear. My reputation was assured. I smiled craftily into my kit-bag and extracted an inflatable lifebelt from its depths.

The mess-boy then informed me that there were two bathrooms aft, one for the engineers and the other for the gunners. He didn't say which was which, so when he had gone about his duties I went through the mess to inspect them. They were identical, or rather one mirrored the other in the strict sense, as one was on the port side of the ship, the other on the starboard, so that things in each were reversed. The idea of a bathroom to be used by only two people was an unexpected treat, but I had to learn to be more stoical. No water came from either of the taps in either of the baths; both rooms were dark and filthy, stinking of urine and seawater. The lavatories did not flush and were encrusted with dirt. I later discovered that Colin's method of cleaning a ship's bathroom was to throw in one bucket of salt water then shut the door quickly. Apparently the bathing method practised by the engineers was to heat a bucket of fresh water on the galley stove, carry it down to one of the bathrooms, then have a wash-down somewhere near it. If these were officers' bathing facilities I wondered what the fo'c'sle crowd's were like. I had heard that British merchant ships were the third dirtiest in the world (the first and second being Greek and French respectively) and it looked as though the *Vesta* was in the tradition.

However, the engineers' mess was a comfortable enough place, with a long table running fore and aft. It had fixed, backed benches on either side and these were thickly upholstered. All the woodwork was substantial oak, darkened by smoke and age. I sat down on one of the padded seats, rolled a cigarette and tried to put a name to the atmosphere suggested by the place. It was that of the smoke-room of an English pub, I decided. At one end of the room was a large mirror in which was embedded a brass chronometer, its glass cracked, the hands immobile. Time frozen to a standstill at a quarter to nine. I smoked and studied the engineers' titles above their cabin doors. These opened directly into the mess, as the gunners' did, but on either side of the room. I wondered what these men would be like, especially the chief who could probably make life hell if he was hell-minded. But what was more important to me was the unknown gunlayer's disposition. As we should be cabined together for months it would be more pleasant if our senses of humour were not too dissimilar. Few men were really without humour, I reflected, but with some it was more difficult to find and to tap, than with others. While thus meditating a lunch gong boomed amidships.

The saloon was similar to the engineers' mess but more spacious more luxurious and with no cabins opening into it. The room was constructed athwartships, not fore and aft as the engineers'. The smoked oak here too lent a comfortable pub atmosphere, or perhaps even that of a three star country hotel. The deck officers' accommodation was on either side of the saloon, separated from it by draughty passage-ways.

The third mate had told me that all the engineers who were aboard were ashore. This seeming paradox arose out of the word "aboard" used technically in this case to mean "in residence"— not on leave. There were, therefore, few of us at lunch : the captain, Mr. O'Neil, Mr. Chapman the second mate, who had just come back off leave, a sullen apprentice about seventeen years old, and myself. I stood by while the others sat down, then took my place at the lower end of the table opposite the sulky youth, where I supposed I was to sit. The apprentice and I were separated from the others by six empty places, but such is the order of things among hierarchies. I noticed that the second mate did not presume to sit in the prodigal first mate's place, despite his absence. Consider that even at that most allegedly egalitarian of tables, the Table Round, there was strict pride of place, I told myself.

The captain always dined in horn-rimmed spectacles. It was the only time he was ever seen wearing them. The three-course lunch, followed by cheese and black coffee, was the best meal I'd had since joining the Navy, and I began to congratulate myself on volunteering for DEMS. Socially the lunch was not a success : Captain Eldrich preyed on his food like some gaunt sea-bird, swooping down suddenly and forking a morsel, then gobbling it quickly, at the same time peering round over the tops of his spectacles as if to catch someone watching him. The second mate, hungry only for the home he had just left, toyed with a chop then left it. He ate practically nothing, shaking his head slowly as the steward offered alternative courses; he hardly spoke at all. The third mate, Mr. O'Neil, was the only one who addressed a few remarks to me, and I was grateful for his attempt to set me at ease. As for the dark apprentice, I might have been an empty place for all the notice he took of me. Later I learned that he was not silent by nature—though he was a rather quiet youth—but that he had recently endured an ordeal at sea after his ship had been torpedoed. He had brought a ship's boat containing six other survivors beside himself some two hundred Atlantic miles, landing on the west coast of Ireland exactly one week after the sinking. He was unaware, as he sat almost frozen to the tiller, that his companions were by this time all dead men. The intense cold on their last night at sea had picked them off, one by one. Only the boy's robust Highland constitution had saved him, and after a fortnight in hospital, followed by three weeks' leave, he was back on one of the company's ships, on his way to war again.

War. Apart from a few bombing raids on Harwich and Plymouth I had no idea what war meant, especially war at sea. I was soon to learn, but meanwhile I was happily unaware. After lunch I was formally signed on the ship's articles, along with two new A.B.s (one a replacement for Redbeard) and one ordinary seaman, then I went to my cabin to write letters. One was to my parents telling them that at last I had joined a real ship, that they might not hear from me for some time, but that they were not to worry. Worry of course they would. In my mind's eye they were sitting before the fire on a winter evening, worrying. But one still used the old formula, partly to pad the filial letter a bit. I also wrote to my old tutor at Oxford, as I'd meant to do ever since joining the Navy. Him I pictured sitting in his quiet rooms, quoting Milton by the page to some first-year pupil who would be staring at the sole of the don's shoe as the gentleman sat in his quotational position with one foot up on the radiator. The sole would be worn in the dead centre, providing a bullseye for the pupil's attention. Snow would be falling softly on Magdelen Bridge and the hibernating punts on the Isis. Then I remembered the date and that it was still the Christmas vacation and that my tutor would probably be at his home near Woodstock, snowballing his large family in the garden.

Suddenly I roused myself from these winter dreams by recollecting that the first duty of a DEMS gunner on joining a ship was to inspect the armament. But then, I reflected, if I uncovered the breech of the 4-inch gun or the 12-pounder they would be snowed on and would rust. No, it would be better to wait for a break in the weather by which time the gunlayer would be there to do the inspection himself. It was his job, as the senior gunner, after all. Thus having satisfied my conscience for the time being I decided to have a stand-up bath, and went along to the galley to heat some water.

In winter the galley was the most comfortable place on the s.s. *Vesta*. It was in the after part of the ship and there was always a splendid fire burning in the stove. On this, thick, sleepy cocoa could be made. I soon found a bucket, filled it with fresh water from the pump on deck, just outside the galley, put it on the stove and smoked until the water was hot. I then carried it below to one of the bathrooms, shaved, and had just started to bath when a cantankerous foreign voice hailed me through the door:

"The gunmen's bathroom is on the port side. Starboard bathroom is for use of officers *only*. Kindly get out, please."

I chuckled at his gangster talk about gunmen, but said that I'd be out in a couple of minutes. When I opened the door I saw a slightly-built, unsmiling man of about forty years of age, towel and soap in hand, bucket of hot water at his feet.

"Sorry," I apologized, "I didn't notice any difference in the two bathrooms."

He pushed past me, saying over his shoulder:

"No difference in bathrooms themselves, but habit makes differences."

This speech was quite a prolix one for Axel Carsen, the Danish second engineer—as I later found out. As a rule he talked in monosyllables, and he seldom talked. He had a silent, bitter hatred for the Germans who had overrun his country. He had not heard from his wife and family since the occupation of Denmark and did not know if they were alive or dead. If he had known they were dead perhaps life would have been easier for him.

I dressed, sprawled luxuriously on my bunk and smoked for half an hour. Life, for the moment, was good. For five months I hadn't known such privacy and I felt a twinge of annoyance when I remembered that someone else was to share this cabin, someone I might not like, and who might not like me. Still, I should hate to have the responsibility of the guns and training the crew, I reflected. The thought of guns made me jump up and put on my duffel coat and seaboots. If it had stopped snowing I would carry out an inspection of the armaments and be able to report to the gunlayer as soon as he stepped aboard concerning their type and condition.

It had stopped snowing. There was a 4-inch anti-submarine gun mounted right aft on a circular steel platform about fifteen feet in diameter and raised four feet off the deck. I brushed the snow off the canvas cover and unlaced the breech covering, then to my dismay I saw that the gun was of a type I'd never even seen before, probably because it was obsolete. Many of the guns mounted on merchant ships in the early part of the war had come from naval museums or been lifted straight out of gunnery drill-sheds. This particular antique had a horizontal sliding breech-block, which in itself was a tidy affair, and I could see that the gun took "fixed" ammunition—that is, with the projectile and its propellant in one piece, like an enlarged bullet and cartridge—not the loose projectile which had to be rammed up the chamber by two men using a rammer, while a third afterwards slid a silk bag of cordite in behind it and hoped that the breech worker wouldn't make a bloody mess of his hands before he had time to take them out. This type of weapon had always struck me as very primitive, even in the drill-shed. With the *Vesta's* Q.F. (quick-firing) gun, one man could punch home the round, thus making the breech close by a trip action while the sliding block pushed his fist out of harm's way. This much I knew about this type of gun, nothing more. As far as its firing mechanism was concerned it seemed more up-to-date than some of the pieces I had been exercised on in Devonport Barracks, but that wasn't saying much. It was in its sighting manipulation, its training and laying, however, that the gun was so archaic. In the layer's position was a sort of hip-girdle or harness into which, I supposed, the layer wedged himself and then traversed or trained the gun with his body. With his left hand he turned a wheel which elevated or depressed the barrel; his right would be on the pistol-grip and trigger. It didn't look easy and I wondered just how difficult it would be with the ship rolling in a heavy swell. I was glad gun-laying was not my job. My place would probably be at the breech, an easy number on a Q.F.

The telescopic sight was in position on the left side of the gun. This was against port regulations because of the possibility of theft or damage, so I unshipped it, stowed it away in a box I found in one of the ready-use ammo lockers, and later took it down to my cabin. Near the 4-inch, in fact slightly overshadowing the gun-platform, was the 12-pounder A.A. gun turret. In the Navy these anti-aircraft weapons were known as H.A. (high-angle) guns, however, not A.A., as on shore. I climbed the short steel ladder and dropped with a clump ! into the chest-high turret where I examined the breech of the gun. It was well greased and in good condition. I was familiar with drill-shed 12-pounders, though I hadn't fired one. It was said that the noise was worse than that of a 6-inch gun and more damaging to the ear drums. I fingered the two ear-plugs in my duffel coat pocket. They were made of rubber and longer than the kind swimmers use. I wondered if one would have time for such personal details before action.

My next visit was to the magazine. This was well stocked and had a flooding arrangement on deck near the 4-inch. There were no machine-guns or small arms of any kind stowed in it, so I went up to the bridge to see if there were any mounted there. None. I bumped into Mr. O'Neil on the way down. He was on the point of throwing a slice of bread to a large, voracious seagull which hovered screaming near the port wing of the bridge.

"I've been looking at the guns," I said. "Is there anything besides the 4-inch and 12-pounder?"

He bit a piece of the bread and chewed it thoughtfully.

"There used to be a rifle," he said. "Think it must be in the chart room—if it hasn't been flogged. I'll dig it out later."

He hurled some bread at the gull which caught it and made off in a long, swooping glide ending in a perch on a ship's taffrail at the far side of the dock.

"There are some 'snowflakes'," the third added hopefully, turning to me.

"Yes. I saw them in the magazine. Are there any smoke floats?"

"Half a dozen, under the gun-platform for the time being. At sea they'll be lashed to the rail, right aft."

I nodded. All that was in order. The "snowflakes" the third had mentioned were rockets usually fired from somewhere on or near the bridge at night during attacks. They lit up the area and showed if any of the attacking submarines were on the surface. They were also used when there were E-boats (German motor torpedo-boats) about, but this sort of attack only happened on the south and east coasts.

"By the way, have you any cigarettes?" the third asked.

I told him that I hadn't, but that I had some ticklers—naval tobacco—left over from my last issue. The third disappeared into his cabin and came out a moment later with a tin of fifty Players.

"The bond's sealed now of course, but perhaps these will last you a day or two," he said, thrusting the tin into my hands.

I started to thank him, but he had gone again with a grin and wave of the hand, so I stumbled off towards the galley to collect some things for tea. Tea, as a meal, was not served on the *Vesta*, but one could get such things as bread, butter, jam and tea to drink from either the saloon pantry or the galley. I chose to get mine from the galley for several reasons. The galley, as I said, was the warmest and most cheerful place on the ship. The cook was a friendly fellow, unlike the traditional ship's cook of fiction who chases the crew out of his galley with a meat-axe every time they show their faces. Colin practically lived in the *Vesta's* galley, warming his skinny body in front of the big stove. At sea there were always one or two A.B.s, the saloon steward and sometimes the bos'n in there playing cribbage or gossiping.

Over tea in the galley on my first day aboard the s.s. *Vesta* I learned that she was no longer a tanker, but had been converted to a grain ship a year previously. The conversion had been a simple one; the tanks, which had formerly contained crude oil, were thoroughly cleaned out and grain was poured into them instead of oil. Last trip, the cook said, they had brought wheat from Canada, and a very good trip it had been with only one sub. scare which had turned out to be a false alarm.

"Where do you think we're off to this trip?" I asked the cook. He shrugged.

"Canada again, maybe—or the States," he answered.

"The States?"

I felt elated, pictured myself moving incognito in my civvy clothes, rubbing shoulders with enemy agents in New York night clubs, perhaps being surrounded by beautiful women at parties and admired for my English accent, which I could always exaggerate, and for my English manners, which I would *have* to exaggerate. It hadn't occurred to me that there were other American ports besides New York which we might go to.

"The States." I repeated, dreamily.

"Or Canada," suggested the cook lightly.

"Or Canada," I sighed heavily.

The cook slid up the hatch of the coal bunker and took a shovelful of coal. As he did so a miniature avalanche occurred and out of the still open hatch shot a decidedly off-white cat, followed by several large lumps of coal and a small cloud of dust. The cat sneezed.

"Sleet," said the cook indifferently, "she sometimes sleeps in there."

The cat shook itself then began to wash itself carefully and systematically in front of the galley stove. I jumped on top of the bunker and sat swinging my consciously seabooted feet.

"When are we shoving off?" I asked, trying to sound casual.

"Oh, in a day or two," said the cook.

He swung a huge iron pot on to the stove and tumbled a lot of peeled potatoes into it, then he poured water over them. Some of it fell hissing on to the stove, driving Sleet underneath a bench with alarm. I was puzzled. To sea in a day or two? The ship showed no sign of readiness for sea. Half the people seemed to be on leave. The mate was still adrift. No gunlayer had arrived from the DEMS place ashore. I wondered if they could possibly have forgotten to draft one? No, it couldn't happen. Perhaps I should give them a ring in the morning, just to remind them? No, I was sure they wouldn't like it. Best just to wait. The G.L. was bound to show up in the morning—if not to-night.

II

DINNER WAS not the melancholy affair that lunch had been. For one thing, the captain was dining ashore with Mrs. Eldrich, so the conversation was less inhibited. For another, the table was almost full. The chief engineer, also the third, fourth and fifth engineers had suddenly come aboard, either back from leave or just shore runs. The second engineer was there too, silent and bitter, so were the second and third officers, the chief steward, the radio officer and his black eye, and now two apprentices. Nature had done a compensatory job of work on the second apprentice. Whereas the senior one was tall, dark, sallow and silent, the second was short, ginger and jolly—in fact insufferably cheerful and hearty.

The chief engineer was a Scot with a faintly parsonic, disapproving air. He appeared to disapprove of the fourth engineer particularly, though it was not easy to see why at first. The fourth was an affable Scots-Canadian with a slow smile and a kind of haggard charm which appealed to everyone, except of course, his chief. The third engineer was a dapper Welshman, furtive and fiery of temper. He had the miniature pugnacity of the Pekinese. The fifth, or Fiver as everyone seemed to call him, was a young Edinburgh man about my own age. I took to him at once. He sat next to me and as soon as his chief had indirectly given permission to talk—by opening a conversation himself with the third —the Fiver began talking to me.

His name was Brian Dunbar and his father was a Presbyterian Minister who had a whisky-still in his cellar. Brian had brought a couple of bottles of the homely distillation back with him. They were safely stowed away in his cabin, which was next to mine. I could help him to drink them, he said, when the chief was on watch. The chief, of course, disapproved of drinking. The Fiver was not yet qualified to keep a watch by himself; he assisted the other engineers during the day watches and had no duties at night, except in an emergency. He was twenty-one years old— the youngest of seven sons.

Here then was the omnium gatherum of the s.s. *Vesta's* saloon, with the exception of the captain, and of the mate whose empty chair I had now come to regard with the kind of awe usually reserved for a Siege Perilous.

After dinner I went along with the Fiver to sample his father's preaching whisky. It was like liquid fire with a dash of brimstone. We drank about four fingers each and I felt as if I could spout a sermon better than Father Mapple.

"This is the stuff to melt the snow," remarked the Fiver.

I agreed that it would melt anything. We drank some more. Each mouthful was a depth-charge.

"I feel like dancing," the Fiver said suddenly. "Let's go up to Rafferty's."

I looked at him. That is to say, I tried to focus my attention on one of him.

"What," I said slowly and carefully, "the hell . . . is 'Rafferty's?'"

"It's a dance hall—not far away. 'Rafferty's Rooms'," the Fiver grinned.

I looked at a drop of the whisky still in my glass. It was colourless stuff, like gin. Bought whisky has been in sherry casks to give it its well-known hue.

"Sorry," I answered, "but I think I'm supposed to stay on board. Only gunner. Stiff upper lip. Straight bat. All that sort o' thing. Got to stand by."

Three or four Fivers looked at me. I hiccupped rowdily.

"Stand by what?"

"The guns, of course."

"What for?"

I couldn't think what for. Nobody could take a 4-inch gun, or even a 12-pounder ashore and flog it. Then I remembered.

"Air raids," I said significantly.

"Nonsense, man, you aren't allowed to open fire at aircraft while in port—not on these ships," the Fiver insisted.

"You are if the order comes through," I corrected him.

"But not if it doesn't," said the Fiver.

"I cannot withstand the battery of such devastating logic," I said. "Let's go—if it isn't too far away."

"No more than a couple of hundred yards. We can nip back in no time at all if the sirens go," the Fiver assured me.

We slithered along the gangway which was quay-level now the tide had dropped. It seemed as if we were leaving a different, smaller ship. The dock policeman at the gate shone a dimmed torchlight on us, demanding to see our passes. We showed him them and then trudged off through the snow, thawing and slushy now, towards Lime Street. There we caught a tram and sat downstairs in the back seat.

An enormous conductress loomed up and toook the Fiver's money. She punched our tickets, hard, handed them to my companion then suddenly turned and stared at me.

"So it's you!" she exploded.

All the other passengers turned round. I looked in alarm at the Fiver, hoping she meant him. But no, she was standing with hands on massive hips, six feet tall, glowering down at me. The Fiver edged away from me slightly. I felt small and isolated.

"Why didn't yer tell me yer were back? Where've yer been? Livin' wi' somebody else I expect! Well?" the Amazon demanded.

All eyes were upon us, feasting on this tramcar melodrama.

"I—I beg your pardon," I faltered, "are you addressing me?"

"I am! And you can drop all them airs and graces, too!" the giant clippy bellowed.

She had a strong, nasal, Liverpool accent. She wagged a forefinger as big as a banana in my face.

"I know who you are!" she shouted.

"Well, then, who am I?" I shouted back.

"Me 'usband, that's who!"

I looked up desperately for a communication cord to pull. Two men up in front burst into loud, Liverpool laughter while the Fiver chuckled with delight, but the women passengers, scenting masculine treachery and infidelity, bared their teeth like Maenads and sat glaring at me tensely.

"What's your husband's name?" the Fiver asked.

"Jim Thompson. 'E knows!" said the clippy, brandishing her heavy metal ticket-holder in my direction.

The Fiver nudged me.

"Show her your paybook," he whispered..

I whipped out my paybook as fast as if there'd been a bayonet at my belly. The clippy shone a little torch on my name and photograph.

"Henry . . . Warren," she read out slowly, then she examined the photograph minutely, "Let's see yer right ear," she said.

The lamp shone directly in my face. I turned my head for the ear inspection.

"No, yer not 'im!" she said, closing my paybook with a slap. "'E 'asn't got a lobe on 'is right ear. I oughter know. I bit it off!"

A great roar of laughter came from all the passengers, women included, this time.

"Do you mind if I have my paybook back?" I asked the clippy.

"Not at all, luv. 'Ere y'are. Sorry I made a mistake."

"Sorry I'm not your husband."

She was just crushing her giant hips between the passengers to collect more fares.

"I wonder if you mean that?" she said with huge coyness, over her shoulder.

"Christ! Let's get off," the Fiver hissed.

The clippy was just beginning a rambling, explanatory yarn to two women about how she hadn't had a line from her sailor-husband for two years (he was the dead spit o' me—'cept for the ear), and as how the Admiralty had assured her that he wasn't dead, but couldn't tell her the name of his ship 'cos of the war, though she still had his allotment, thank God.

We stood up and the conductress rang the bell. The tram ground to a squeaking halt; we got off. I breathed deeply the cold Liverpool air, a free man again.

"We've gone two stops past. Blast you and your bloody wives!" the Fiver grumbled.

"Fiver, you've just saved my life. The paybook was a brilliant idea. I don't know how to repay you," I said.

"I do," he answered, "there's a boozer just across the road. Never say things like that to a Scotsman."

I saw his point when he ordered a large whisky for himself and allowed me to pay for it. I had half a pint of beer, but on the second round the Fiver generously reversed the order so that I then had a double whisky too. It wasn't as good as the Reverend Dunbar's hot-gospel stuff, but it sufficed to keep the cold out.

Rafferty's was packed with soldiers, sailors, merchant seamen, Polish airmen and women of all colours, sorts, shapes, sizes and ages. There must have been five hundred all told, for Rafferty's had been a small cinema at one time and there was plenty of floor space. A bomb had recently fallen next door on a warehouse and had peppered the ballroom walls with shrapnel, the marks of which were plainly visible. It gave the scene a slightly heroic, devil-may-care atmosphere. As we dumped our coats in the cloakroom I said to the Fiver :

"I say, I can't dance very well. Does it matter ?"

He grinned, and shrugged.

"Sassenachs don't know how to dance anyway," he said.

"It's odd," I answered, "that the Celt should consider himself so inferior to the Anglo-Saxon that he must forever be stating his superiority over him."

"You wait till it gets around the ship about your missus the clippy," the Fiver menaced.

"If it ever does I'll punch your rather prominent nose," I said cheerfully.

"Well, if we meet any more women you've deserted you can bail yourself out," the Fiver retorted as off he went on to the dance floor, a mousy-haired partner suddenly materialized in his arms.

A quintet played furious music at the far end of the room on a raised platform. Smoking, I watched the sweating, jiving couples trying to keep pace with its riotous off-beat rhythms. The bass player's hair hung long, lank and black down over his face, veiling it completely as he slapped, punched and spun his instrument, hurled it away and hauled it back to himself like a reluctant partner in a jitterbug. The pianist was etiolate, dark-haired, with rimless glasses, a drooping cigarette and probably a graveyard cough. the drummer had the traditional appearance of exuberance and animation. A beefy man with big fists, he held his drumsticks in a ludicrously genteel manner, the little fingers of his hands fastidiously crooked. There was something offensive as well as funny in this attitude—a mockery of manners. An elderly man with puffy red cheeks chortled and tootled happily on a saxophone, while the tight-lipped trumpeter who sat behind him seemed to be trying to blast the most obvious toupee I had ever seen in my life off the sax-player's head.

A pole with elaborate manners asked a girl for a dance. He bowed so exquisitely low that before he had time to right himself a sailor had whisked the girl away on to the floor and was dancing with her. The airman gaped, a courtly phrase in suspension, then an expression of rage crossed his face. He smiled quickly at another girl, clicked his heels Nazi-fashion, silently embraced her and they danced grimly off, he stiff as a lobster, she breathlessly out of step.

"What, a sailor not dancing?" a voice said at my elbow.

A small, middle-aged woman was smiling up at me through a cloud of cigarette smoke.

"I'm not a very good dancer," I apologized when we got on to the floor and I tried to waltz.

The little woman's hair was dyed chestnut and nauseously perfumed.

"That's all right, dear. I'll take you round," she said.

I held my breath and somehow got round the floor without once treading on the woman's feet, though I suspect that this was due to her nimbleness. The band stopped for a breather and the bass-player gave his instrument a final spin, stopped it, tossed back his hair, produced a bottle of beer from the pocket of his tails and proceeded to gulp its contents mock-surreptitiously underneath the piano. Hardly anyone noticed and nobody laughed. I saw the Fiver and his mouse talking to another girl so I made for them, first having excused myself. My partner seemed relieved to see me go.

The Fiver had apparently told the girls his name was Robert and that mine was Tom. I wished he'd thought of something more original and dashing for me, Raoul or Torquil, for instance. Or even Roderick. The other girl was dark and attractive. She spoke in a gentle voice and laughed pleasantly. I hoped the Fiver was set on his mouse.

"We didn't exchange names," I said to the dark girl, dancing

"No," she smiled, "Milly's friend said you were called 'Tom', but I didn't believe him—from the way he said it. You aren't a 'Tom,' are you?"

I shook my head.

"I'm a Henry."

She laughed delightedly.

"I'm a Helen."

"Was yours the face that launched a thousand ships?" I ventured, taking some of the might out of Marlowe's line by my adaptation.

The answer came pat from the non-literary mind.

"No, but it's sunk a few."

It was my turn to laugh, but a fight had broken out at the other side of the room and was spreading rapidly in our direction. The Rafferty Band, however, were used to rough-houses. Up they jumped and played the National Anthem, twice. Everyone in the room patriotically froze—the drunks swaying like kellys—until the dirgelike chords died away, then the band broke into a quickstep and the brawl began again, more fiercely than before. Helen looked frightened.

"I want to go," she said.

We went to the cloak-room to get our coats and found the Fiver there with Milly. They already had their coats on.

"Let's get out of this dump," the Fiver said thickly through a muffler he was winding about his neck and mouth.

We all thought it a good idea. Helen was apparently staying with Milly—an admirable arrangement from our point of view. But when we got outside into the cold dreary night, Milly announced that the last tram had gone and we should have to walk.

"Where do you live?" we asked her.

"Down by Alexander Gate," she said, shivering quickly.

"The docks," groaned the Fiver, "and it's four bloody miles!"

"Your two hundred yards," I grumbled.

But I was glad they didn't live in some other direction. At least we went the same way. We trudged through the snow and slush, Milly holding on to the Fiver's arm, but Helen and I aloof from each other. Milly told us a rambling yarn as we walked along and this helped to pass the time. She had been, she said, an A.T.S. driver in France and had been evacuated from Dunkirk with the Tommies. During this ordeal a machine-gun bullet had ploughed through her shoulder and she had been discharged from the Army, given a medal and a small pension. It sounded a most improbable story and I formed the opinion that Milly was not quite all there. However, she promised to show us her bullet wound as soon as we reached her house. This was because the Fiver had immediately expressed disbelief in the story, swearing that either she had made it up, or that it was the story of some film which was showing in the town. He and Milly walked on ahead arguing; I turned to Helen.

"And have you any battle-scars?" I asked.

"No, and I wouldn't show them to you if I had," she answered flatly.

So that, I thought, is that.

Milly's house was in a dismal dock street which even the snow had failed to enhance much. There were only two rooms, one up and one downstairs. The electricity had been cut off as Milly hadn't paid her last bill. She lit a stump of candle and stuck it on the table, then she found another stump, lit that from the first, warmed its bottom and stuck it on the mantelpiece. The room was small and squalid with peeling wallpaper, flaking plaster and laths like naked ribs sticking out of one corner of the dirty-brown ceiling where the plaster had collapsed. It looked as though someone had put a foot right through it. The sink was chipped and cracked, piled with dirty dishes and plates, some with the remains of meals on them, days old meals. The room was furnished with one backless chair, a three-legged stool, a broken sofa and a small, wobbly table. On the mantelpiece were cosmetics, hairgrips and a teacup without a handle. Under it was a line of wet washing, mainly underwear. The fire was out.

"Can you get it going?" Milly asked. "There's some firewood in the corner."

I took my coat off, noting as I did so that Helen was looking round strangely, as if she were seeing the place for the first time. This struck me as rather odd.

"I think I'll keep mine on a while," she said quietly when I moved to help her off with her coat.

There was some coal, as well as a few sticks on a newspaper and after several attempts I managed to make them catch fire in the small grate. Milly, overcome by a sudden sense of propriety, it seemed, took down the washing which was beginning to steam. Helen and I sat on the creaky old sofa while Milly pottered about making tea, with the Fiver pretending to help her. On the table was half a loaf, some magarine, a lot of crumbs and an opened tin of milk, weeping and sticky down the sides.

"Tea up!" the Fiver said briskly, after a while.

Milly offered the milk tin but I declined it, saying that I always took tea black. Helen said the same. We all crouched by the fire, sipping the boiling liquid, and looking thoughtful. After she had drunk her tea Milly yawned and stretched herself, catlike, then announced that she was off to bed. We could sit by the fire all night if we wanted to, but she had to be up at seven to go to work. She was a waitress in a Lime Street café. Milly opened the stairs door, said "Goodnight," and up she went.

"She's forgotten the candle," said the Fiver. "Perhaps I'd better take it up to her?"

"Most considerate of you," I said, glad that he was going.

He followed Milly upstairs and shut the door after him. The absence of the candle which the Fiver had taken made little difference to the light of the room as the fire was now burning brightly.

"I think I'll take this off now," Helen said.

I helped her off with her coat. We lit cigarettes and smoked for a while in silence. My feet were wet and the slight alcoholic effects had worn off long ago, leaving me tired and depressed. But Helen looked quite fresh and delightful in the firelight. She kicked off her shoes and curled up her legs on the sofa : I noticed for the first time that her legs were long and shapely. My tiredness vanished in a flash and I forgot my feet. She leaned forward to stub her cigarette so I draped my arm on the back of the sofa in such a way that it would be in an immediately comfortable position around her as soon as she sat back. The ancient trick worked. Helen looked surprised, but not alarmed and seemed to accept the situation very well. Good, now for the second move, I thought. I leaned forward to kiss her, but she gently fended me off. I pulled her gently towards me, but she gently resisted. I tried a combined pulling and leaning movement, but the girl was still froward. She turned her face away with a wincing expression so that I became annoyed and conscious of my wet feet again. I folded my arms and with a sigh, sat apart in masculine frustration.

"I'm sorry," Helen said quietly, "I'm afraid you mustn't. It isn't that I don't like you, it's just, you see, that I'm married."

I sat upright with a jerk.

"Not two of you !" I exploded.

Helen smiled, puzzled.

"Well, it takes two to make a marriage, doesn't it?" she said.

"No, I didn't mean that," I answered, and had to tell her the conductress story.

The girl laughed, and the conductress seemed a long time ago. Helen fumbled in the chaos of her bag then produced a plain gold ring which exactly fitted her matrimonial finger.

"See?" she smiled.

"Yes," I grunted.

From upstairs came the sound of muffled scuffles and protestations. Milly was apparently putting up a token resistance. Helen looked uneasily round the room.

"It's the first time you've been here, isn't it?" I said.

She nodded.

"I didn't know it would be as bad as this," she answered.

We lit cigarettes and she told me her story. She was a lace-maker from Nottingham and had come to Liverpool for the week-end to see her soldier husband, only to find that he had left for Ireland—Belfast—that morning with his regiment. Disconsolate, but not wishing to return to Nottingham the same day, she went into a café and there met Milly who served her and listened, as it was not a very busy hour, to her tale of woe. Milly then offered to put her up for the night, but suggested that they should go out and enjoy themselves in the evening first. So they went to Rafferty's.

"But I should have thought if you had worn your ring it would have kept the wolves away," I commented.

Helen smiled tolerantly.

"You're not a wolf, or you'd know it has the opposite effect," she said.

"Well, what about your things?"

"My clothes? I left a bag at the station. I'm catching the eight-thirty home in the morning—I mean *this* morning. What time is it now?"

I looked at my watch.

"Half past two. You'd better get some sleep," I suggested.

She yawned unobtrusively.

"I think I will, if you don't mind."

She pronounced "you" as "yo." I got up and she stretched herself on the sofa, smiled gratefully as I put her coat over her, then closed her eyes, like a contented child. I thought of Gower's simple, moving line : "The beaute faye upon her face," then suddenly I felt tired and depressed, so I decided to go back to the ship and try out my new bunk. As I was going through the usual sailor's struggle to get my coat on without having someone to hold the blue jean collar down, the air-raid sirens began to wail. Helen opened her eyes and sat up.

"You're not going, Henry?" she asked anxiously.

The inland towns had not suffered much from bombing at this stage of the war. The girl had probably never been in a raid, hence her genuine alarm.

"Sorry, but I have to. I'm supposed to be on board in case of fire—near the ammo you know," I answered, as casually as possible, for I did not like the idea of being near ammo when fire-bombs were dropping. I didn't hear Helen's reply for at that moment the Fiver came blundering down the stairs.

"Come on, man !" he shouted, grabbing his coat and opening the street door at the same time, "Duty calls !"

"Goodbye, Helen. Don't worry, it's probably a false one," I said, trying to reassure her.

She looked frightened, but lay down again.

"Good luck," she said, and smiled.

We were out in the street, the moonlit street, and the snow looked blue.

"A bomber's moon," the Fiver grunted, looking up at the full, pale face.

"Which way?" I asked.

"Down."

We ran down the street, slipping and sliding over the cobbles, then we crossed the main road and on towards Alexander Dock. As we slowed to a fast slither I gasped :

"What's all the hurry?"

"I'm on fire-party to-night. Just remembered when the sirens piped up," the Fiver explained.

"You're much more conscientious than you pretend."

The Fiver chuckled.

"It's my particular brand of hypocrisy. By the way, how did you get on?"

"Oh, all right," I muttered, not wanting to give details, "What about yourself, did you see the wound?"

My ingenuous question fully deserved the bawdy answer it received. The dock policeman shone his dimmed lamp at the Gate.

"What ship?" he demanded.

"*Vesta.*"

The password sufficed. We went through the gateway as search-lights wove shifting patterns in the sky : the drone of distant bombers, followed by their crump, crumps, deadened our foot-steps on the ship's gangway. The third officer was by the stern with a hose rigged near the magazine. One or two seamen loitered on deck, smoking behind cupped hands, their faces glowing like demons.

"Glad you weren't too far away," the third said to me. "Looks like a raid on the docks."

I swallowed hard. The man was doing my job and this was my first night on board. If it had been an R.N. instead of an M.N. ship I should now have been doubling away under close arrest.

"Thank you—for lending a hand, sir," I stuttered, "with the hose—and everything."

"That's all right. I'm supposed to be the gunnery officer any-way," came the dry answer.

Well, now I knew who the gunnery officer was. The bombers droned nearer and it was now clear that they were coming for the

docks. Incendiaries had already started fires in the docks' hinter-
land, markers for the second wave of planes carrying the big
high-explosive bombs. Army ack-ack was on the job and as the
Jerries began to pass overhead a cruiser in the next dock opened
fire with her high-angle guns and multiple pom-poms, the latter
always referred to at that time as "Chicago Pianos." The noise
was deafening, but there was comfort in it, for us, though not for
long. A stick of incendiaries landed on the wharf-shed next to the
Vesta. The shed burst into flame from end to end.

"On hoses!" yelled the third.

The Fiver turned on the hose near the magazine and I led the
nozzle-end over the gun platform to the other side of the ship,
There were six hoses all told, but the pressure was not very great
and we could only just reach the wall of the shed nearest the ship.
We seemed to be just piddling uselessly up against it until the
N.F.S. arrived. Soon we could see their powerful jets streaming
up and onto the blazing roof. Once or twice they soared too high,
overshot the roof and came crashing down on our decks, drench-
ing everybody to the skin.

"'Ere, turn it up! Want us ter catch our deaths?" shouted a
cockney seaman.

"Get the gangway heaved inboard," the second mate ordered
some hands, then he stopped and pointed: "No, wait a minute,
Jesus Christ! Look!"

We all turned towards the gangway. Coming up it, cap on the
back of his head, singing at the top of his voice, was a man with
the biggest shoulders I'd ever seen. In his arm he carried what
looked like two large bottles. He stepped on deck, and the Fiver
nudged me.

"The mate," he said.

Here was the mate of fiction come to life: grizzled, big-
shouldered, ham-fisted, bull-voiced, in fact with all the meaty
attributes one reads about in sea stories.

"Mr. Campbell!"

The captain's voice squawked down from the bridge through
a megaphone. The chief officer of the s.s. *Vesta* stopped singing
and looked round.

"Did somebody mention ma name?" he asked.

"Mr. Campbell! What the devil have ye got there, man?"
Captain Eldrich screamed.

The mate looked aloft.

"It's all right, sir," he yelled back, "ah'm just aboot to dispose
o' them."

He walked towards the port side and suddenly hurled the two
objects, one after the other, far into the dock.

"Not like the mate to throw away good booze like that," the Fiver commented, some time later.

"Booze?" the third mate who had just been having a few words with Mr. Campbell laughed. "Those were two unexploded incendiary bombs!"

The big mate was now amusing himself by squirting at the shed with a hose in each hand. The water pressure had been increased and we too were able to help the firemen with our hose. Unexpectedly the shed collapsed inwards with a huge whoof! and we could now see the firemen on the other side. We cheered them and some of them waved their axes at us. We could also see the cruiser, with the gunners in their anti-flash gear and the ammo-parties dashing about the decks.

The second wave of bombers droned nearer and at the sound of a thin whine, unpleasantly near, we all threw ourselves flat down on the deck, all except Mr. Campbell who was still playing with his hoses. The H.E. bombs fell in the neighbourhood of Milly's house, probably on it, as well as on many others in those poor streets. The Fiver and I looked at each other as we got to our feet, but neither spoke. The cruiser's Chicago Pianos were playing again, the firemen were climbing aboard their engine, off to another fire, and the mate, Mr. Campbell, was away to his bunk.

At four-fifteen the all clear sounded. We stowed the hoses and other gear, then went below. In the engineer's mess, crouched under the table with a face as white as moon, was Colin.

"Get to hell out of it!" snarled the chief engineer, "and make some coffee."

The Fiver beckoned me into his cabin. He handed me a glass of his father's preaching stuff and poured one for himself. We drank in silence, then the Fiver poured another.

"Happier days," he said, lifting the glass to his lips.

We drank. I felt sick and horribly tired.

"Do you think that lot got them?" I asked.

"Aye, Henry," the Fiver answered, looking about ten years older. "Wiped out the whole area, I'd say."

"Ought we to go and see—to make sure?" I suggested, hopelessly.

The Fiver looked at me incredulously.

"Are ye bloody daft, man? Nobody's allowed ashore now. We're shoving off with the tide. You saw the sign."

"The sign?"

"The mate. He's come aboard. All shore leave's cancelled and I'm going to turn in. Got the forenoon watch with the second, so good night, or rather, good morning."

I blundered off to my own cabin, my head spinning with the

whisky. Once inside I peeled off my wet gear and left it where it fell, then I made a half-hearted attempt to towel myself and finally clambered on to my bunk where I slept long and deep.

When I awoke we were at sea.

III

I T W A S about ten in the forenoon and my head felt as if it were being sawn in half, an effect which was probably produced by a mixture of late night, heavy smoking, preacher's whisky and the shattering racket made by the rudder-chain overhead. As I lay there listening to its thrashings I tried to focus my eyes on some familiar object. They finally settled on my duffel coat swinging on its nail beside the bunk and I watched the rhythmical movement, fascinated. Then a chain of associations started up somewhere in my partially blacked-out mind. I sat up in the bunk and looked wildly round the cabin, then leaned over and peered into the lower berth. No gunlayer! I leapt out of the bunk and dressed hurriedly in overalls and seaboots. There was some water in a can by the wash basin so I sloshed some into the basin and had a quick cold wash. As I was drying myself I caught a glimpse of a white, haggard face in the cracked mirror. The eyes were red-rimmed, the thin, fair hair matted, while from the unshaven chin and chops sprouted an incipient tawny beard. The strange-familiar face was mine.

As I dragged on my duffel and crammed a rolled balaclava on my head as a cap, I rapidly rehearsed a speech intended for the captain's ears : there's been a mistake . . . I'm not qualified to take sole charge of a gun's crew . . . only a seaman-gunner . . . never even been to sea before . . . never even fired a big gun. That would rock him, the old bastard! He would have to turn back to put me ashore somewhere. Serve him right! I felt bitterly against this insane world which had draft-chitted me into this difficult and frightening position. Frightening? Yes, I was scared all right, but as my anger cooled I began to wonder if fear had after all given me the necessary dutch courage to rush up to the bridge and blurt out my pathetic tale to the captain and ship's officers. I had always suspected myself of moral cowardice and even as I wavered now I knew that I could no more put myself in such an ignominious position than fly a Spitfire or make *crêpes suzette*.

I sat down on the edge of the bottom bunk and listened to the big beat of the ship's engines and the lesser, intermittent throbbing of the telemotor which operated the rudder every time the quartermaster spun his wheel a few degrees. The ship had a sickening motion and I doubted whether I should enjoy the cigarette I was trying to roll with shaking fingers. Then I remembered Helen and the bombing. Had it really happened? It had the quality of a dream to me now, but Helen was probably dead, and Milly with her. Milly and her tin of sticky milk. I thought of Helen's bag waiting at Lime Street Station, and nobody claiming it. Perhaps it would be there for years, with all the things rotting inside.

"God, what a trivial bloody mind I must have!" I said aloud, not knowing then that the mind often strays into triviality during crises and tragedies, perhaps as an escape.

The cabin was alive. Everything bumped, swayed, jigged, swung or rattled idiotically. I opened the door and looked in the mess. Colin pottered about with a broom.

"Yer've missed breakfast but ah've saved ye some toast. There's tea in the galley. Ah couldna waken ye at eight bells."

"Thanks Colin."

I tossed him a cigarette, took the toast on deck and threw it to some hungry-looking gulls that piped and wheeled about the stern. We were just clearing the mouth of the Mersey and it was sleeting unpleasantly. Two or three cargo ships seemed to be steaming with us and we were now just losing sight of the land. I stepped into the galley for a mug of tea and information from the "wireless," as galley gossip is called.

"Now don't get in my way," said the cook, but quite pleasantly, "I'm now preparing dinner for the fo'c'sle, and lunch for the saloon."

He grinned. I wondered if there was some intermediate term for the engineers' midday meal. The cooking stove ran athwartships and there was a long bench opposite. Upon this I sprawled. The cook indicated a large enamelled teapot on the stove. I got up and poured myself a mugful, then sat down again. The tea was horribly stewed and tasted like lye. I made a face.

"Try some sugar," the cook suggested, handing me a tin and spoon.

"Your mate missed the boat, you know," he added.

I stopped ladling sugar into my tea and looked up.

"The gunlayer?"

"S'pose so. He was on the wharf with his hammock and bags just as the tugs were pulling us out. The Old Man wouldn't stop to take him aboard. Kept bawling through his trumpet that we'd already got a gunner."

"By God! Doesn't the silly old fool know that a ship of this size is supposed to have two gunners? Why the devil couldn't the DEMS have sent the G.L. yesterday?" I stormed.

"It wasn't their fault," said the cook, more rationally. "The sailing orders were changed. We weren't supposed to shove off until to-morrow, but we suddenly got this lot to commodore up to Oban where we'll pick up the Western Ocean convoy. The Old Man thinks he's an admiral now o' course, just because he's got three Johnny the Greeks to look after. Wouldn't be a bit surprised to see him wearing a cocked hat and sword for the next few days."

I glanced through the open doorway on the lee side. Two of the Greek ships were keeping station with us on that side, one on the other. I sipped my tea and smoked.

"Bloody glad to get away from Liverpool anyway," the cook went on, "it ain't safe in that place."

He saw me looking at the Greeks.

"Have to watch out if you meet any o' those fellows ashore," he said slyly.

"Why?"

He laughed.

"Cor, ain't you innocent!"

I didn't take much notice, but guessed that there was some implication of homosexuality. There was. I later learned that all merchant seamen considered Greek seamen homosexuals. The jokes on this subject were innumerable and interestingly varied, but I wondered why they had originated. There seemed to be some classical tradition in the merchant service regarding Greek morals and habits. But then, why not? A great number of merchant seamen I met were surprisingly well-read. There seemed to be at least one self-educated W. H. Davies on every merchant ship, a man who spent much of his leisure time in serious reading, and visited libraries and museums ashore whenever he could.

"None o' them speaks English," the cook said, pointing to the other ships. "The Old Man's been bawling at 'em through his meg. when they've come too close, but they don't take no notice, just grin and wave their arms about. Happy lot o' bastards they seem."

It was more likely, I thought, not heeding the cook's comments, that jokes about Greeks had been handed down orally throughout the centuries. Tales of seamen were as old as, well, the Greeks.

The cook raked some ashes out of the stove and then lifted one of the top lids off.

"Mind putting some coal in?" he asked. "I make everybody work who loiters in here during the morning."

I shovelled some coal from the bunker into the stove.

"Thanks, have a fag," said the cook.

A thought suddenly struck me. We were at sea and I didn't

know who was in my gun's crew! I went at once to the gun-deck-
to-bridge telephone, a toy which was housed in a little box fixed
to the side of the 12-pounder turret. The wind was blowing hard
and it would be difficult to hear, so I raised the hood of my duffel,
lifted the receiver and put it inside the hood, next to my ear. I
stood back to windward and twiddled the little handle. Almost
at once a voice rasped:

"Bridge. What d'ye want?"

"Could I speak to the third officer, please?"

"And who the hell are you?"

"The gunner."

"Are ye now? Well, come up to the bridge. Ye sound like
Donald Duck over this gadget! The third's below for a spell, so
ye can have your word with me," said the voice.

"Thank you, but who are you?" I asked.

"Who d'ye think I am, Rabbie Burrans?"

All Scotsmen have a strong literary sense, concerning Burns and
Scott.

"No, the first mate, I should imagine," I answered.

"Then your imagination's no playing ye false. On your way,
laddie."

I hurried along the flying-bridge, wondering why the third
wasn't on duty. Normally the third mate keeps the eight to twelve
watch, both morning and evening, with the captain. Perhaps he
was having a late breakfast and the mate was looking out for him,
as he himself would no doubt have overslept. (This turned out to
be true.) Up the ladder I went to the bridge itself. The surly
apprentice was on the starboard wing, the captain on the port. I
was glad I'd chosen to come up the starboard ladder.

"Mr. Campbell?"

"Chart-room," answered the monosyllabic apprentice.

The chart-room was abaft the wheelhouse. I went past the
quartermaster at the wheel and knocked on the door jamb, the
door itself being wide open, fastened back on the catch. The room
seemed full of Man.

Mr. Campbell seemed much older than I'd expected from his
behaviour of the previous night, but then I'd only seen him at a
distance in fire and moonlight. He was about fifty and his thin
sandy hair was turning white at the temples. His face had weathered the four winds, been scorched by a thousand tropical suns
and pelted with northern hail and rain for thirty-five years. Add
to these ingredients enough liquor to send six ordinary men in
search of Alcoholics Anonymous and see what colour you get! Not
even Rubens could have mixed it. Moreover, the subtle changes
brought about by different lights on his face were a wonder to

behold. With the dull grey light of the chart-room port breaking on it his face was suffused with some of the varied colours one sees on moors in autumn. He had a wide mouth chopped straight across his face and whether stern or smiling it hardly changed its shape. Only the cold grey eyes really expressed the first mate's moods, or rather the puckering, ageing skin around them did. On his head he wore, guardsman fashion, a peaked cap bearing the company's insignia, or house flag. The huge oilskin which came nearly down to his ankles had additional shoulder pieces like epaulettes and these emphasized Mr. Campbell's immense breadth.

Tales of his capacity for living, of his tremendous strength and violent temper were famous among seamen, but mainly because he himself was a master of seamanship. I had heard many of them already, on the galley wireless; how he was once shipwrecked off the Horn during a gale, and how he had managed to cling to a raft for three days in huge seas until he was picked up—the sole survivor of the clipper-ship which had been homeward bound from Australia with its cargo of wheat; how he had been torpedoed three times; twice in the First World War, once in this, and how he had on one occasion hurled a captive U-boat commander back into the sea for spitting contemptuously on the bridge and calling him an "Englander"—probably the biggest gaffe the Nazi ever made, and certainly the last.

Normally a first mate "carries the ship on his back," as they say. That is, he has to run the ship, maintain her, and supervise the loading and unloading of cargoes in port. The latter of course Mr. Campbell never did, and were it not for the fact that this enormous sea-going Highlander was such a superb seaman, and handled the crew so well at sea, no ship's captain would have suffered his negligence in port—so the galley wireless informed me. (Incidentally the mate never touched alcohol on board the ship). On the other hand, if he had been more attentive to port duties and played up to the company's men ashore, he would have had a ship of his own to command many years before now.

These things ran through my mind as I watched Mr. Campbell bending over a chart, apparently unaware of my presence in the room. His breath was visible in the cold attentuated air as he muttered something about "bearing north five," then he straightened up and peered at me as though through a mist.

"So you're the new gunlayer?" he said.

"Seaman-gunner, sir. The gunlayer missed the boat, I've been told."

He looked at me shrewdly and clacked his tongue as if it tasted sour. Then he said, not unkindly :

"Is that what's worrying ye?"

"Not much, sir," I lied. "But I'd like to know who's in the gun's crew, besides myself."

"Aye. That's natural enough," the mate answered dryly, scratching his head with a pencil. "Ye've no been told?"

"No, sir."

"There's maybe a list somewhere," he pondered, stroking his big, grizzled chin.

"Tell ye what," he said suddenly, "give the klaxon a jerk or two and see what happens. I'll let the captain know you're sounding action stations for gun-drill purposes."

I'd noticed an old klaxon horn fixed to the 12-pounder turret, but at the time could think of no reason for its existence other than as a seagull-scarer.

"Very good, sir," I said, and turned to go just as a fist as big as a boxing glove suddenly shot out and punched me not too gently in the chest.

"Are ye no wearing a lifejacket?" the mate growled.

"No, I didn't think it necessary yet, sir," I answered.

"Well maybe it's no necessary yet—but you get one on all the same!"

"Aye, aye, sir," I said, turning to go once again, but being stopped once again.

"Got one of ours, a kapok waistcoat?"

"No, mine's a pusser's."

"A fwhat? Oh, one o' them rubber Navy things. No good for keeping out the cold. Get one o' the ship's—from the chief steward."

"Thank you, sir."

I escaped from the chart-room at last and made my way aft towards the 4-inch gun and 12-pounder. The klaxon was a rusty old gadget with scabs of paint peeling off it. I jerked the short bit of lavatory chain hanging from it.

"Errrk!" it went, but pianissimo.

"Errrk! Errrrk!"

Louder and better. I tried again.

"Errrk! Errrrrk!"

Fortissimo. Splendid, but the klaxon was now swinging from my hand on the end of the chain, jerked clean off the turret! The swinging slowed to a dangle and I felt as if I'd caught a rabbit by the ears and didn't know what to do with it.

There was a wooden boat-deck above and forward of the gun-platform. On this deck was one ship's boat swung outboard on its davits. This boat was for the use of the engineers, the gun's crew and anybody else who happened to be aft and unable to get forrard in an emergency. By the boat, clutching a small suitcase and wearing both a kapok lifejacket and an outmoded Board of Trade cork one, stood quivering, Colin the mess-boy. Whey-faced, he peered anxiously down at me.

"Are you in the gun's crew?" I shouted up at him.

He nodded vigorously.

"Well, the gun's down here," I said.

He came down to the platform and stood looking sheepish. I pointed to the bag.

"Going off somewhere?"

Colin explained that he thought the klaxon meant "Abandon Ship," so he grabbed his "panic bag"—a suitcase packed with essential gear which nearly all merchant seamen kept handy in case of going "over the wall" in a hurry—and went to his boat station.

"Like a good boy," I said, acidly, transferring some of the mate's power to myself for a brief moment, no doubt to compensate for having just having been under that power, and mating it over the mess-boy. "Well, it hasn't happened yet," I went on, enjoying myself, "I'm just trying to find out who's in the gun's crew and who isn't."

Colin brightened.

"The cook isn't," he said, trying to be helpful.

I cursed him roundly, matishly. Later I realized that Colin was as necessary on that ship as the scapegoat was to the Jews. Or perhaps it would be better to compare him with a lightning conductor; all one's immediate hatred and bad temper went to earth through him, and left him, apparently, unscathed.

One by one five other men appeared on the gun-platform, all men who had no essential jobs in time of action : the saloon steward, the second cook, two young ordinary seamen and the bos'n's mate, a thick-set fellow named Baines. He looked about thirty and well-seasoned. I decided at once that he should be my number two on the 4-inch. Number two was a responsible position as the duties included supervising the loading, breech-handling and reporting the gun ready for firing to the gunlayer who then fired when he was ready, or when he wasn't ready if he was nervous or trigger-happy. Number two also had to be ready to deal with misfires and give the order "Still !" This order could be given by any member of the gun's crew if anything went wrong, and at that order everybody froze to immobility—rather like in the game called Statues—until the fault was discovered, put right, and the countermand given, "Carry on."

The men obviously disliked being turned out simply to be counted.

"Ought to get some overtime for this," grumbled one of the young seamen, a pimply fellow about nineteen years old, "I was off watch."

"Better see the mate about that," I answered. "He ordered the round-up because he didn't know where the list was with your names on it."

"Don't suppose there ever was a list," muttered the second cook, a squirrel-faced, secretive Welshman with limp, black hair. "That's the trouble with this packet. No system. Never was."

From my experience up to date. I was inclined to agree with the sciurine second cook. Colin opened his mouth to say something, but then saw the huge figure of the mate billowing along the flying-bridge, and shut it again.

"Well, Gunner, are they all present?" Mr. Campbell growled.

"Yes, sir, they're all here," I answered, then drew him aside, lowering my voice. "The mess-boy, is he much good, sir? He seems inclined to panic and even if I put him as an ammo supply number where he wouldn't upset the others, I don't suppose he could lift a projectile, let alone carry one."

The mate nodded in agreement.

"Baines, get one o' the A.B.s up here," he ordered.

"Aye, aye, sir," said Baines.

"Not a quartermaster, mind," the mate added.

Baines hurried away to the fo'c'sle and came back with a black-bearded pirate about his own age whose hands were like mule hoofs.

"Ah, Johnston, ever been on a gun's crew before?" the mate asked this picaresque and most able-looking seaman.

Johnston nodded.

"Loading number on the last ship, sir."

I imagined his big fist punching home the ammo.

"Very good. Well, now you're on this one—whatever number the gunner assigns ye to. Got that?"

Johnston nodded, but looked neither elated nor dejected at the idea. The mate went on, casting his eyes from one to another of them :

"And ah hope ye'll pay attention, all of ye, to what the gun-layer here tells ye to do, and make sure ye get up here fast when the alarum goes—Hullo, fwhat's that?"

He broke off sharply and eyed the klaxon dangling from my hand.

"It came off," I said. "It's the klaxon."

The gunners guffawed loudly.

"Chippy!" the mate bawled.

A tubby old man with a red face like a professional Father

Christmas pottered towards us, oilcan in hand. The oilcan in fact never seemed to leave his hand. I had seen him often, moving about the stern of the vessel in his tattered oilskin, dropping blobs of oil on everything that moved, squeaked or rattled, and I had actually wondered, rather apprehensively, if he was anything to do with the gun's crew. The knowledge that he was the official ship's carpenter came as a pleasant surprise. His bright blue eyes twinkled under the snowdrift eyebrows as the mate told him to "Fix the hooter."

"And when you've finished that job, Chippy," Mr. Campbell ordered, "ye can oil the taps in the officers' bathroom. They squeak like a pair o' damned mice."

The mate strode off and Chippy pottered over to where I was standing.

"If ever you want any oiling done, you let me know, son," he wheezed. "Ain't very little chippying to do on ships nowadays, 'cos they're mostly metal."

He tapped the turret significantly with the spout of his oilcan, then went on :

"But the owners don't seem to realize it yet. An oilcan expert, that's what I am. I keep the steering gear in good order and I take soundings in the ship to see if she ain't leaking."

"Don't you do any carpentry, then?" I asked, incredulously.

"I see that the hatch-covers fit properly," he said, "and on this ship there's only one hatch with wooden covers, so that don't take much looking after."

He shuffled off to fetch a screwdriver.

"Don't take any notice of 'im, mate. Barmy, that's what he is," Baines commented.

"So you'd be if you hadn't been ashore for thirteen years," put in the second cook.

"What was that?" I asked.

"It's the truth," answered Baines," Old Chippy ain't set foot ashore nowhere in thirteen year—not even to have hisself a piss."

I thought this about one of the most unlikely tales I would ever hear, but it was perfectly true. The carpenter had joined the *Vesta* in 1928 and had never set foot on any dock, quay or wharf since. He had got out of the habit of going ashore, he told me later. It didn't feel safe "on the beach." Once when the ship had been fumigated owing to a suspected smallpox case, Chippy had collected some food, climbed to the crow's-nest and stayed up there for two days until the fumigating was over and the rest of the crew had rejoined the ship. The crow's-nest was the enclosed, pillar-box type, quite dry and comfortable, but rather cramped.

"Well," I said to the men, "gun-drill as soon as the weather eases up a bit, then I'll see what positions suit you best."

They nodded, and to Baines I said :

"Think I'd like to try you as number two."

He grinned.

"Suits me. You can put me anywhere so long as it ain't in front of the muzzle," he said.

The s.s. *Vesta's* gunners sauntered off to their quarters and respective duties. As I watched them go I wondered what it would be like trying to drill such a haphazard lot up to some sort of standard of efficiency. Not that I was efficient, that was half the trouble; I didn't even know what the guns would sound like and it gave me the palsy to think what might happen when I tried to lay and train the 4-inch by myself in that unique harness, arrangement, with the ship rolling and pitching on a dark and stormy night. My only consolation was that perhaps submarines didn't attack during rough weather as they found it difficult to sight and fire their "kippers."

The engines began to slacken their pace as the small convoy ran into a bank of fog. It had stopped sleeting but the fog was damp and cold. It was impossible to pick out any details of the Greek ships on either side of us; only their dark outlines were visible and I could see that the third vessel seemed to be dropping astern. As I made my way towards the chief steward's store I noticed that a lookout had been posted on monkey-island, a small platform above the bridge which contained some navigational instruments and wireless gear. Later I could see two lookouts in the bows and one at the stern. The fog was closing in.

The chief steward was a Yorkshireman with a puffy red face, straw-coloured hair and a wild accent.

"Ef this bluddy fog keeps up we shall miss t'convoy at Oban and 'ave to wait up there abaht a week in t'perishin' cold afore we get another," he grumbled as he tested the red light and clipped it on my new kapok jacket.

There was a battery in a waterproof case which fitted into a pocket of the jacket. The idea of the red light was to enable potential rescuers to see the survivor in the water at night. I dragged on my duffel and fastened the toggles with difficulty, owing to the thickness of the lifejacket underneath, then tried to cheer up the gloomy chief steward.

"Never mind. Perhaps we'll be able to have a run ashore."

He looked at me severely.

"Young man," he said slowly, "have you ever been in t'Firth O' Lorne?"

"Can't say I have," I answered flippantly. "Is it a pub?"

"No it isn't a bluddy pub! It's where t'Western Ocean convoys form up—most on 'em anyway. It's easy to see you 'aven't been on this run afore," he snorted.

"Well, there has to be a first time, hasn't there?" I said hotly.

The chief steward suddenly put on a Wilfred Pickles act, became friendly, confidential:

"Now, sign your name in t'book for t'jacket, lad. And doan't take on. What's your name, eh?"

I hated this kind of unctuousness, following so closely upon rudeness. "Lad" didn't please me much either. I'd celebrated my twenty-first birthday in a friend's rooms at Christ Church during my last term at Oxford, and so thought myself past the lad stage.

"You'll be able to read it in a minute," I said, answering the steward and adding my scrawl to a page of signatures under the heading: "Lifejackets (Complete) Issued," in a greasy ledger.

"Henry Warren," the steward read slowly. "Oh, so that's it? A nice name is Henry. I like it."

"Keep it then," I said, pushing the book towards him.

He dated the signature and initialled it, then I went off to see if the snowflake rockets were stowed near the bridge. They were in a long metal chest or locker, together with some .303 ammunition for the rifle, and the rifle itself, under the starboard wing of the bridge. There were also brackets fitted to shoot the rockets from.

"Needn't bother about those," said the second mate, suddenly appearing behind me. "We ship 'em at dusk and unship 'em at dawn—just as the good book says."

I thanked him and took the rifle down to my cabin, along with a hundred rounds of ammunition.

Lunch among the engineers had a curious semi-formality about it. While we were at sea anyone was allowed to wear overalls at table, but to my amazement Colin waited upon us in an immaculate white jacket buttoned up to the neck. He was, moreover, quite an efficient waiter and had been trained, I think, as a *commis* at a Glasgow hotel. Apart from the fact that the chief's place was at the head of the table there seemed to be no other order of precedence, at first. However, I sat down at the first vacant place I saw and had just begun to eat some pea soup as thick as fog which Colin had put before me, when the third came out of his cabin. He stormed at the mess-boy:

"Next time, see that nobody sits in my place!"

"I beg your pardon," I said, half-rising from my seat. "It's really my fault. I didn't know this was——"

"No, but *he* did," glowered the third as Colin scuttled off to his pantry. Then he turned to me:

"It's all right, man," he said, "the grub tastes just as bad wherever you sit, but that mess-boy gets slack if you don't jog him about something every day."

Nevertheless, I could see that the Welshman was uneasy in the place lower down the board.

"Look, I don't really feel easy sitting in a third engineer's place. Let's change," I suggested, although I would have felt easy sitting anywhere, except in an electric chair.

"Well, all right then," the third agreed. "Mind if we change places, chief?"

The chief, who had been watching the affair with his customary sour disapproval, shook his head slowly.

"Ye can change your trousers for all I care," he said tartly.

The third and I changed places and he smiled happily in his own.

I felt as if I were back at school. Who was to sit where was a thing we always squabbled about at meal-times.

The fourth was drinking coffee, his greasy knobbly elbows resting on the table. He had been first in to lunch and it was nearly time for him to relieve the second in the engine-room. In his quiet Canadian drawl he asked lazily :

"Any idea where we're headin' for this trip, Chief?"

"Not for one of our dominions," replied the chief, without looking up.

Remarks about "our dominions" and the national shortcomings of "colonials" were often made by the chief when the fourth was present.

"As a matter of interest," the chief went on, pausing to make sure of a full audience, "as a matter of interest, we are going to Baltimore, for maize."

The fourth looked across at me and smiled his weak, good-natured smile.

"In my neck o' the woods we call it 'squaw corn'—from 'indian' corn. Get it?" he said.

"Isn't that the stuff they give to chickens?" the Fiver asked.

"Yes, us chickens. They put it in the bread now," the third answered, then he leaned back and said distantly, as if in answer to another inquiry, "Baltimore, yes, I've been there. Not a bad place. Not as good as New York of course, or New Orleans, or San Francisco, or. . . ."

He reeled off the names, showing his acquaintance with a number of American ports. But the chief cut him short.

"Or Buenos Aires, or Archangel, or Yokahama, or Timbuc-bloody-tu," he snorted. "If you'd been to them all as often as I have you'd know that there's nothing to choose between 'em. All of them stinks of loose women and drink, and that's not all. . . ."

Here we go again, said the expression on the Fiver's face as he glanced across the table at me. The chief enumerated at length the respective demerits of all ports in the world, except Glasgow. When he had left the table and gone below to see how the engines were taking the slow revs. we all relaxed and lit cigarettes. The third leaned forward, and looking furtively round said :

"Does anybody know how Japanese women masturbate?"

We shook our heads. Nobody, except the third engineer—and presumably Japanese women, knew. His description of this esoteric Oriental vice was so amusing that its obscenity was almost killed and we roared with Rabelaisian laughter, until the second engineer came into the room. His face was haggard and dirty; his dull, tragic eyes gazed uncomprehendingly at us. To walk into a room full of laughter is often uncomfortable; for the second it must have been appalling. Our laughter quickly died away.

"Fourth, the chief wants to see you, please," said the second, sitting down wearily to begin his meal.

As the fourth got up we all excused ourselves and I went to my cabin to mug up some gunnery notes on quick-firing guns. I had no notes or information about the *Vesta's* type, where the layer and trainer were the same person, but I managed to modify the standard 4-inch Q.F. drill, after which I spent the rest of the afternoon memorising the results until I was sure I wouldn't make an ass of myself at the first practice.

Owing to the fog and the time of the year it got dark early; because of the war we were not allowed to show lights, use the siren or contact the other vessels by wireless. Needless to say, in these circumstances we lost all three Greek ships before midnight. The captain was furious, but could only curse and blame the fog, and of course, everybody on the ship.

My first night at sea passed uncomfortably. As I was to be the sole occupant of the cabin for this voyage I had spread my belongings and decided to sleep in the bottom bunk. Even so, in the lower birth the vibration was still great and the rudder-chain thrashed without mercy the deck overhead. I had been warned that it was dangerous to close the two-inch thick door of the cabin, in case the ship was hit by a bomb or torpedo, or in the event of her striking a mine, because such impacts were likely to twist the ship's timbers. This often caused doors to jam if they were shut, turning the cabins into tombs, if anyone happened to be inside them. When ships were built during the war some thoughtful marine architect designed hardboard crash-panels to be fitted in the lower half of all doors. A kick from a seaboot, a rapid crawl on all fours and you were a free man, relatively speaking. However, the s.s. *Vesta* was a peace-time ship and her doors were of mighty oak. We kept them either wide open, or hooked ajar.

When my door was on the hook there was a gap of six inches between it and the frame. Through this gap drifted the sickly smell of warm oil from the engine-room, which did not help matters for me. As we rolled slowly up the Irish Sea and into the North Channel, making an average speed of five knots, I tossed and turned green on my bunk. Once, at about one in the morning, I got up and went on deck. I saw nothing apart from the black fog, but the smell of it was a change from that of oil. After falling over a deck-pipe which ran along the port quarter, however, I stumbled back down to the cabin, cursing.

By morning the fog had lifted, or we had run out of it. We increased speed to twelve knots in an attempt to catch up with the convoy from Oban. The sun was making a brave effort to shine as we passed the Mull of Kintyre and we continued northward until about noon, then turned due west. I was on the gun-platform watching the rough outline of Islay disappearing, when the phone rang. The captain wanted to see me on the bridge. When I got up there Captain Eldrich was pacing the boards, his old spindly legs encased in waterproof trousers, and slightly bent at the knees. Occasionally he would stop to give an order down the pipe to the engine room.

"Ah, Gunner," he exclaimed when he saw me standing at a respectable distance, "owing to the fog we've missed the Oban convoy. However, we shan't let that worry us, shall we? We don't want to hang about in the Firth waiting a whole week for another one, do we?"

I shook my head dumbly to all these rhetorical questions. The captain was in an unbearably hearty mood, as was usual after he had been in a cantankerous one.

"No," he went on, "we don't. So I've decided to sail the ship to the United States on her own, that is to say, independently, solo, you understand? Good. Well, you know what this means, Gunner? A sharp lookout must be maintained—especially about the hours of dawn and dusk. At such times the U-boats may be on the surface charging batteries and you can then bring your armaments to bear on them, provided that they are in range of course. Oh, by the way, I don't want this to get round the ship as it may cause undue alarm : there's a German raider—a pocket battleship—operating somewhere in the North Atlantic, so keep a sharp lookout, Gunner. You may be able to get one or two shots into her. You never know !"

I gulped. A pocket battleship ! Did this man really expect me to take pot-shots at it with our obsolete peashooter? Apparently he did. It was not the sort of thing he joked about, as I later discovered. He had a diluted sense of humour anyway and the only laughter his jokes ever evoked was sycophantic, subordinates' laughter.

As I was passing the galley door on my way back to the guns, the second cook popped his head out.

"Have you heard all about it then, man?" he said.

"About what?" I answered cautiously, mindful of the captain's warning about the need for secrecy.

"That we're going to try an independent crossing in spite of the fact that there's a German pocket battleship knocking around somewhere?"

So much for security measures on the *Vesta*. The galley wireless operated quite well on the bridge's wavelength, apparently. I must listen in more often, I thought, but said with forced nonchalance :

"Oh, that? Yes."

And pretended to laugh. We were now six or seven degrees west. Until we reached about 25° west, roughly 1,200 miles away, we should be in danger of submarine attacks. Beyond 25° west operated the German battleship later identified as the *Admiral Scheer*, the raider which had attacked the *Jervis Bay* convoy on Guy Fawkes' Day the previous year. I went below and smoked a cigarette, considering the situation, not that there was anything I could do about it—apart from keeping a sharp lookout, as the captain had ordered. I felt nervous and depressed, but the deep depression was more cosmic than personal. A great wave of hopelessness and helplessness seemed to overwhelm my spirit, then suddenly I thought of Voltaire's famous advice. I must cultivate my garden. My garden in this case was the gun-deck. I resolved to get the mate's permission to have both a 4-inch and 12-pounder drill that afternoon.

IV

THE DRILL was better than I had expected. It was not up to Whale Island standard of course, but for a haphazard crew led by a green, acting-gunlayer it showed promise. I arranged to have a gun-drill every afternoon at six bells, weather and other conditions being favourable, and I felt confident that after a few of these drills we should have reached a fairly proficient stage. I hoped too, that the captain would give his permission for us to have a practice shoot when we were out of the main U-boat area. This was chiefly because I wanted to test my re-action to gunfire and to observe the crew's—if I were in a fit state to do so.

During the first drill I found, as I'd expected, that the greatest difficulty was in laying and training the gun by oneself. I had to stifle a tendency (born of long hours of practice in the barracks' gunnery school) to give orders to the trainer to train the gun round so many degrees to port or starboard. The habit had become ingrained, a reflex action, hard to break. Eventually I compromised by muttering an order to myself then pushing the gun round with my hips in the harness, but often, if the ship rolled too much, I had either to wait until she rolled the way I wanted to swing the gun, or get two of the crew to shove the barrel round. This, training against the ship's movement, proved to be the biggest curse of all. The fact that it was an impossible task for one man when the ship rolled heavily made me consider re-modifying the drill so that one member of the crew would be free for barrel-pushing. Later I managed to get another of the deck crowd recruited to the gun's crew and this was his sole occupation. He was a barrel-shover. It was easy enough to get the gun round to bear on a target using the long barrel for leverage.

The bos'n's mate, Baines, proved to be an excellent man on the breech of both guns, while the black-bearded Johnston was equally efficient as the first loader. He handled the practice ammunition lightly and easily so that I had every confidence that he would handle the live stuff expertly and without fear.

For four days we ploughed westwards, into the U-boat zone. The weather was fine; crisp and clear. We drilled each day for an hour, mostly on the 4-inch. We saw no other ships, no sign of submarine or aircraft, although I kept strict dawn and dusk watches. I began to be less apprehensive; perhaps we should be lucky, perhaps they only attacked ships on the way home when they were heavily laden with war supplies or food. Perhaps.

On the fifth morning, just as I was thinking of dismissing myself for breakfast, I heard the sound of an aeroplane engine. Errk! Errrk! Errrrk! went the klaxon as I tugged the bit of chain. I phoned the bridge to ask them if they could see anything. They had binoculars, I none, and suspected that they had probably been flogged by Red Beard. The alarm bells sounded for action stations and the third mate assumed his role of gunnery officer.

"Unidentified aircraft, bearing green nine oh," said his voice down the telephone.

The gunners were already scrambling over the 12-pounder turret and grabbing tin hats from their pegs. I leapt over after them and jumped into the layer's position. We saw the aircraft speeding towards us, low on the starboard horizon.

"Load!" I shouted.

A round of H.E. was punched home and the breech closed. I

fixed the nose of the aircraft dead in the centre of the cartwheel sight and waited for the range to shorten. The fact that there was someone in the plane never occurred to me. It was simply a black speck which kept moving out of the centre of the sight, disturbing the pattern. I hissed at the young seaman on the other side to train more to the left. The speck was getting bigger as the range shortened and I gave the usual warning:

"Stand by!"

The 12-pounder was fired from the breech by the simple method of banging the fist down on the flat-topped firing arm at the right hand side. Crude but quick. The aircraft was in range.

"Fire!"

As I gave the order I bit the chinstrap of my steel helmet, then my eardrums nearly split. I'd forgotten to plug my ears.

"Cease firing!" I must have yelled, though I never heard myself.

Three whitish puffs of smoke appeared to the right of the aircraft, followed by three distant bangs. The aircraft banked and peeled off course, away from the smoke puffs, so that we could see its markings: red, white and blue rings. The phone rang and Johnston answered it.

"Cap'n says not to shoot. One of ours," he said.

I nodded. As we stood down and I saw to the sponging out of the gun and the stowing of ammo I felt very depressed. I had acted according to orders, that is, opened fire on an aircraft which did not show its identity before coming within range of our guns, but it did seem ungrateful to the R.A.F. men who were only coming to see if we were a lost sheep, a straggler from some convoy. I felt they would be justified if they complained loudly about it.

But the men in the Hudson were apparently used to being shot at by trigger-happy sailors. Anyway, they didn't complain. On the contrary, apart from the usual inquiries as to the identity of our ship and the reason for our not being convoyed, they signalled: "Congratulate gunners. Good shooting. Made us sweat."

Our practice had been successful, then, but it was twenty four hours later before I could hear properly. I went down to the mess and tripped over a foot which stuck out from under the table. Colin's. We stared at each other from our respective horizontal positions.

"Is it—all over?" Colin gibbered.

"Yes. We've just sunk the pocket battleship with three rounds from the 12-pounder."

Clearly Colin didn't believe me. He crawled out from under the table and we both stood up. I saw that he was carrying a cup of coffee which hadn't spilt.

"My breakfast?" I inquired.

"Yes, and there's some toast if ye want it," Colin answered.

I took the toast on deck and threw it to some gulls, smaller birds now, not so well-fed as those nearer land. Real travellers these were; deep sea boys.

After a week's steaming from the coast of Scotland we reached 25° west and considered ourselves clear of the U-boat fringe. Moreover, there had been no news of the raider. It was probably farther south, looking for convoys. The captain had wisely steered us on a north-westerly course and we were now about 60° north, on a line with the southern tip of Greenland, Cape Farewell. Soon we would turn south-west and head for Canada and the United States, our destination.

Life on board the s.s. *Vesta* was pleasant enough for me, a mere passenger in the eyes of the merchant seamen, but now that the submarine danger had lessened, and there had been no news of the raider, the crew began to discover and be less tolerant with one another's faults. Petty jealousies arose and there was the continuous grouse about the food and the accommodation on the old tanker. The chief steward was a pinching, scraping, niggling, mean old bastard who starved the hands to amass a small fortune upon which he would retire and live at ease after the war— according to the crew. This was a conventional sailor's picture of all chief stewards and partly justified. There may have been honest ones, but I never met any of them. All the chief stewards I ever sailed with indulged in sharp practices of one kind or another, usually at the expense of the crew.

The *Vesta's* new hands compared the ship unfavourably with their last, but then last ships are always better than present ones. I tried to remain aloof and not get enmeshed in the very intricate web of gossip and slander that is woven around nearly every member of a ship's company at sea, when there is nothing else to think and talk about, but it was extremely difficult to live apart. A ship is a floating village. Nothing in the world is more parochial than a ship out of danger.

The third engineer battled with the chief steward over the paltry fact that the Yorkshireman would never send down to the engineers' mess the kind of sauce that the third always lusted after. There was an argument during which blows were exchanged and shouts of, "And I'm fed up with *your* bloody sauce!" came from the stores, then out came the third with a bleeding nose, followed by the chief steward with two red eyes which later turned blue-black.

The chief engineer severely rebuked his subordinate who lapsed into a deep Celtic sulk for many days. The only thing he had said in his own defence was :

"Well, he asked for it if ever a man did. He would keep sending down Heinz Tomato when he knows I only like Daddy Sauce."

At the lunch the day after the big fight a quart bottle of Daddy Sauce gleamed enormously on the table in the third's place.

"There," said the chief engineer sourly, "An ah hope it'll mak ye sick. Daddy Sauce, bah !"

I wondered if it was any better at sea in peace-time when nerves would not be so taut. Baines assured me that if anything it was worse.

"Nothing else to fink about," he said.

Once I had action stations sounded and brought the 4-inch gun to bear on what turned out to be the dorsal fin of a porpoise. I had mistaken it for a periscope. Once I stood, helpless and fascinated while a silvery, torpedo-shaped object headed straight for the ship at high speed. I shut my eyes tight and said a quick prayer—one for the road. Nothing happened. I could still hear the beat of the engines and the sea's noise. I opened my eyes cautiously and was just in time to see a whale-calf swerve blithely away from the ship's side and disport itself in our wake, titillated no doubt by the swirls, currents and eddies set up by the propellers.

At seven bells on the morning of the eighth day we altered course to west by south. I had grown accustomed to the lashing of the rudder-chain overhead and the slow, rolling motion of the ship, so that I now slept soundly when not on watch. I was in fact sleeping when the alarm bells rang and woke up with the nostalgic idea that the noise was made by my alarm clock at home. At first I groped about blindly, trying to turn it off, but when I realized that this was *not* home and that the ringing was *not* caused by my old alarm clock I came awake smartly enough, put on my lifejacket which I'd been using for a pillow, dragged on seaboots and duffel coat, then went off up to the guns in a blundering rush. Baines was already clearing away the 4-inch for action; Johnston was opening the ammo lockers; other gunners were racing along the fore and aft bridge towards the guns. As I wedged myself into the layer-trainer's position I looked at Baines.

"What's the buzz?"

"Sub—on the surface—dead astern—'bout five miles," he muttered through taut lips.

I adjusted the telescopic sight and squinted down it : nothing but sea, and as the stern lifted with the swell, grey sky, then sea, then sky again—and the cross-wires at the end of the telescope. Then I saw it, a small dark smudge on the ocean's face, at first. I made a rapid sight adjustment and there it was again! It was more clearly defined this time, a small grey craft, bows towards us, conning tower plainly visible. Half-sick with fear and excitement I gave the order:

"With H.E., load!"

I heard Baines open the breech and the sound of Johnston ramming the round home, then the slur and click as the breech slid across and Baines locked it with the breech-mechanism lever.

"Breech closed. Ready."

Baines's unruffled report in matter-of-fact tones did something to reassure me, but still a thin saliva began to well up into my mouth—the sick-lubricant. I spat it out and prayed that I wouldn't be sick now. My stomach felt full of curdled milk and I expected to burst my bowels at any minute. Fortunately no such catastrophe happened, nor was I sick. The range was an impossible one for an old 4-inch gun so I stood upright and tried to relax for a while. I wondered if I dare smoke a cigarette for bravado's sake, then I decided not to as it might not be good for discipline, and what was even worse, it might make me vomit.

After having given the engine-room orders for all possible speed, Captain Eldrich strolled down to the guns, leaving the first mate in charge of the bridge. The Old Man was wearing his uniform cap, proving his sense of occasion. For everyday wear at sea he usually sported an ordinary civilian flat cap, with black and white checks.

"Don't open fire yet, Gunner," he advised me, "we're just hoisting the colours."

A seaman was bending a tattered Red Ensign on to the halliard of the short flagstaff on the boat-deck. He hauled it up and the ensign broke out suddenly like a dull red puff of smoke. Its flapping edge was as frayed as a tramp's trouser-bottoms but the captain smiled happily.

"Good old Red Duster," he said heartily, then his face once more assumed its habitual expression of melancholy.

I tried to remember where I'd seen such a face as his before. It was a striking face, not because it was either ugly or handsome, but because it looked simply dead. It was the face of an extinct species, it—yes! I remembered now. It was the face of the Tollund Man, the Iron Age corpse found in a Danish peat-bog, preserved by the surrounding chemicals for hundreds of years, but dead, most dead. I had seen a photograph of him in a periodical before sailing. His dark skin was stretched bat-taut across the bones of his face, like the captain's.

"Open fire when ready, Gunner," the Old Man sang out suddenly.

"Waiting for the range to shorten, sir," I answered. "No sense in wasting rounds we might need later."

"Quite true, quite true," agreed the ancient Master Mariner. "We leave it to your discretion, then."

"Thank you, sir," I said, keeping my telescope eye on the submarine and hoping that my discretion might make up for my lack of valour.

As I kept the submarine under focus, trying to estimate whether the range was increasing or decreasing, the captain spun me a rambling yarn about how he had rammed and sunk a U-boat in the 1914-1918 War. Although it seemed an inappropriate time for line-shooting anecdotes about World War I, which was ancient military history to me, a tale told by my father in his cups, the Old Man's narrative actually had a soothing effect on my nerves. The story was involved, but his manner of telling it calm and unhurried, and some of his assurance seemed to pass into me. He finished talking and, it seemed, for want of anything better to do, wandered off back to the bridge. The third mate had his binoculars trained on the target.

"Range doesn't seem to alter," he grunted. "She seems to be keeping up with us. Must be a twelve knotter, one of their big boats, a U-cruiser—or whatever they call 'em."

"Wouldn't be out this far if she weren't, would she, sir?" Baines commented respectfully.

"Might be a 'Milch Cow'—a supply submarine," said the third, angered slightly by Baines's remark.

"I wonder if she could be one of ours?" Johnston said, half to himself, no doubt remembering the Hudson incident.

"If she isn't, she could be one of theirs," muttered the second cook, with a certain amount of logic.

"Run out o' tin fish, most like," said Harris, the pimply deckhand. "Goin' to 'ave a bash at us wiv 'er guns—if she can get close enough."

This sounded likely. It would be a good match as far as the guns were concerned. Theirs would be about the same size as ours, but the unfair thing was that we presented the bigger easier target.

"Well," said the third mate, dropping the binoculars onto his chest. "It's up to you, Gunner, so open fire if you want to find out."

"Right, sir," I answered.

This was it. A real gun-battle with a surfaced U-boat in daylight! It was every gunlayer's dream—but I was only an acting-gunlayer. To me it was a nightmare.

I lay and trained the gun as best as I could on the small target.

"Stand by," I cautioned, rapidly depressing the muzzle as the stern heaved upwards.

I squeezed the pistol-grip and shut my eyes as my finger tightened on the trigger. As the long grey barrel shot forward it seemed as though an express train were rocketing through some windy station and taking me along with it. The noise was not so bad, but the blast from the business-end of the gun gave the feeling of being socked in the face with a hard pillow. As the barrel recoiled with a tremendous, shuddering jerk, the whole gun-platform shook visibly and half the hip harness fell with a clatter about my feet. I kicked it out of the way and through the telescope saw a spout of water where the projy had ploughed into the sea. It was short, about a thousand yards. Must have depressed too much, or not put enough on the range-sight, I thought. Incidentally, besides laying and training the gun I had to set the approximate range on a small dial, a job which on most 4-inch guns was done by a member of the gun's crew called the sight-setter. But actually I preferred the present way as it saved time.

"Short," said the third, spotting. "Up eight hundred."

I raised the sight eight hundred yards, hoping to straddle the target. The next shot would still be short, the one after that would be over, then we could start dropping down in four hundreds and going back up in two hundreds. It could go on for ever—or until the ammo ran out, for who could hope to hit a sub. bows on at this range with such an elderly weapon as ours?

Suddenly there was a flash of light from the submarine. I thought for an instant that she was signalling—until a spout of water rose into the air about two hundred yards from our port quarter, and we heard the dull boom of the U-boat's gun. She was firing back, the battle was on!

Wild with excitement we fired ten rounds, three of which burst within two hundred yards of the enemy. The U-boat fired back about the same number of rounds with no more success and, eye to the telescope nearly all the time, I was only vaguely conscious of their fall of shot and this mainly through shouts from our gun's crew as the spouts rose to port and starboard of our stern. Both the German gunlayer and myself were sighting on each other's gun flashes and this of course made the firing rapid. Still the range only altered imperceptibly. It was even more difficult trying to train the gun now, with half the hip harness missing. I had to put my shoulder against the protective shield on the side of the gun and inch the barrel round in that manner if I wanted to train left, or for a right bearing grasp the shield with both hands and pull.

The gun had just been loaded with the eleventh round when the captain ordered us to cease firing and use smoke floats. Meanwhile he would see if the chief engineer could squeeze another couple of knots out of the old tub, even if it meant burning the mess furniture to do so. Six smoke floats were lashed to the rails round the *Vesta's* stern. They were about as big as dustbins, painted a drab green and when ignited would give off clouds of dense black smoke which on a fairly windless day provided an effective smoke screen. When smoking the floats could either be left on deck, or you could chuck them overboard. As shots from the U-boat's gun fell a hundred yards or so short of our stern we unlashed three floats, set one of them smoking then heaved it over the stern into our wake. The other two followed after five minute intervals. At the same time the engineers contrived to make black smoke pour from the *Vesta's* funnel as the ship pounded along flat out at thirteen knots. We altered course and zigzagged irregularly to add more confusion and in a short while nothing could be seen astern except a long black cloudland. We altered course several times during the next two hours and lost the U-boat completely. I had a great respect for "dustbins" after that. We hoped the smoke from them had choked the Germans. Perhaps it had, for we never saw them again!

I now considered myself a fledged gunlayer, having fired one gun in practice fashion, the other in an action of sorts at a U-boat. But I couldn't help thinking that the North Atlantic was rather too harsh a gunnery school, for me. However, I had satisfied myself that I could carry on under fire without being too scared to think clearly and I had noted, perhaps with a slight regret, that the gun's crew didn't seem too scared either, so I had nothing to feel superior about, no one to tower over except Colin who was later found coiled among the thickest mooring ropes he could find in the forward rope-locker, right up in the ship's bows. Everyone towered over Colin, but then, I wondered, were we superior? It was a wonder to me that he went to sea at all with his kind of nerves. None of the armed forces would have accepted him for service because of his deformity and general ill-health; he had given up working in hotels and joined the M.N. at the outbreak of the war, and when he wasn't being scared to death by battle noises he was suffering at the hands and tongue of practically everyone on board. To me, Colin was the hero of the ship. I resolved to treat him with more respect in future.

Next day we managed to get some more practice with both guns when some icebergs drifted by. High explosive shells fired from the 12-pounder at a range of seven hundred and fifty yards sent up showers of glittering ice-green fragments, providing us all with what the captain called "an interesting spectacle." One round from the 4-inch actually split one of the smaller icebergs in half and we could hear an echo on the ship's plating—the horrible wrenching sound of breaking ice—as the undersea part of the iceberg cracked mightily.

But soon we were to witness another kind of interesting spectacle, for as we cleared the sub-arctic zone that night a gale blew up and mountainous seas swept the *Vesta* miles off her course. It was impossible to sleep in the cabins aft as the stern heaved out of the water and the screw whickered in the air, causing the entire after part of the ship to vibrate like a gigantic springboard. At times I thought that the rudder-chain would smash the deck-head of my cabin, so great were its thrashings, but somehow it was still in one piece three days later when we found ourselves in calmer waters. During those three hurricane days hardly a word was spoken in the mess. Colin struggled down from the galley with anything the cook had managed to prepare. Usually it was corned beef sandwiches or biscuits as the galley fire was continually being extinguished by seas breaking in, every time the vessel was pooped.

The poor cook was driven nearly mad by these sudden inrushes of water. One morning when I looked in the galley he was perched on the bench holding his apron up, like a woman afraid of mice, while water a foot deep swirled about the deck, looking for an exit down the scuppers.

At first I enjoyed the rough weather; it was a shield against enemy attack, yet it gave one something to strive against which I found exhilarating. But lack of hot meals and continually being drenched to the skin, together with the mad writhings of the old ship which made sleep impossible, soon sickened me of the storm. The only person who seemed to enjoy it was the bos'n. He was a short, chunky man with long dangling arms and a prehistoric shamble. His wide mouth with its thick lips broke quickly into smiles, displaying a set of powerful teeth whose whiteness was intensified by the dark hue of his skin, his crisp black hair and eyebrows. When not actually "working the crowd," sleeping, or furtively preparing the rope he was going to sell at the next port, the bos'n spent his time in the galley. He seemed cheerfully obsessed with the idea that the ship would founder before reaching Baltimore, or on the homeward run, and he had a recurrent doom-line which ran thus:

"She's a bastard. She's a bitch. She's a bloody old humdinger and she'll break her back, that's certain, mark my words. You'll pay off soon you blokes and you'll find lodgings in the Seamen's Bethel—Davy's bloody locker down below!"

His square thumbs would be turned down, in case anyone should doubt the direction Fate—and the bos'n—intended us to go.

"That's a nice way to talk about the only ship you 'ave under yer feet," cracked Harris, one of the ordinary seamen, on one occasion.

Many of the crew resented the bos'n's attitude, superstitiously regarding it as a temptation which Providence would not hesitate to seize upon. I must admit that the bos'n's presence often made me uneasy, while his jeremiads had such a disturbing effect on me that after a time I began to avoid the man.

During the gale I spent as much time as I could in the wireless room amidships. This was pleasant for two reasons: there was less vibration here than in the stern, and the wireless operator was an unusually amiable fellow. Like myself he was regarded by the fo'c'sle crowd as little more than a passenger on the ship, though they seemed to get on well with him. He did not keep a watch, but worked an eight-hour day and it was during these hours that most signals were sent out. The *Vesta's* radio officer was not the traditional mad sparker of maritime fiction but he had a number of peculiarities. He sported a black, neatly trimmed moustache which was no bigger than an eyebrow and this, together with a contrived sartorial elegance earned him the title of The Count, on board ship. The Count was everything a seafaring man is usually not; he was unmethodical and careless about everything except his appearance and of course his wireless equipment. He was notoriously efficient with women and had managed to avoid marrying any. The bulkhead of his cabin was papered with photographs of girls—not pin-ups, personal acquaintances —of almost every nationality. He even had a picture of a tiny muffled figure standing outside an igloo. The Count was only about thirty, but he had packed the erotic experiences of several normal lifetimes into his score-and-ten. That is to say, this is the impression one had on hearing him talk, for his conversation was mainly about women, particular women, though occasionally he would consent to discuss them in the abstract.

"Women," the feminist would muse, "Women. Everything that has ever been said about them is true. Women are fairies and witches, angels and bitches; they are fascinating and irritating, mean and benevolent, kind and malevolent, faithful, deceitful, vicious and virtuous, profound, shallow, absurd, hateful and adorable; they are also elemental, primitive and provocative."

The Count would then put his feet up and lean back in his swivel-chair, smoking elegantly in spite of the roll of the ship.

"Women," he would continue, "are depressing and exhilarating, tedious and titillating; they are. . . ."

"Are you suggesting," I once cut in when he had nearly exhausted his supply of adjectives, "that women are paradoxical?"

He appeared to turn the word over in his mind very carefully, as if it were an explosive or an egg.

"Paradoxical," he said at last, slowly pronouncing the syllables. "Yes. Women are Creation's most successful paradoxes."

After this ex-swivel-cathedra pronouncement he sat smoking and smiling at his picture gallery.

"Why not marry one of them?" I suggested.

He almost leapt out of his chair.

"Good God, man!" he shouted. "Do you think I want to lose my soul?"

After the storm we rolled on a gentle swell past Newfoundland at a steady ten knots, until we ran into some fog banks. Speed was then reduced to five knots as there was often convoy traffic on the shipping lanes from Halifax, Nova Scotia, which we were just about to cross. Double lookouts were posted as the *Vesta* chugged through the fog, for though at times the visibility was about three hundred yards, at others it was no more than fifty The sea was dead flat and the closeness of the fog made us feel that we were living in a small, intimate world. It was also a silent, intense world and we were all on edge as darkness fell and our engine speed was reduced to three knots which made our movement in the still waters almost imperceptible. There was no sound apart from the slow, muted throb of the engines, an occasional whir from the telemotor, and the whisper of water along the ship's sides.

In the galley at midnight I was trying to thaw out after peering from the 12-pounder turret for the previous three hours. I was heavy with fog. It hung about my brows and eyelashes and I seemed to be panting it out of my lungs, clouding the galley. I lit a cigarette to change the atmosphere and was just enjoying the first deep pull when a sudden blast from the ship's siren nearly made me choke with fright and smoke. The noise was followed by a splintering, tearing, iron-twisting, wrenching racket from somewhere in the fore or 'midships part of the vessel. Almost immediately after this the *Vesta* shuddered slightly, then began to heel over to starboard. I left the galley by the port door, much faster than I'd entered it. Megaphonic voices shrilled and one of them seemed to come from somewhere out in the fog and not on the ship. This alarmed me. I was even more alarmed when the bows of another ship, much bigger than ours, suddenly loomed up on the port side. Somebody at the top of this wall of steel flashed a torch and shouted something incoherent. I noticed that the ship carried a paravane boom and that things were tangled with, and dangling from it. The strange ship also heeled as she scraped along our side, then she sheered right off, taking with her, as was later discovered, the port wing of the s.s. *Vesta's* bridge. It was this and other wreckage that I'd seen snarled and twisted round her paravane boom.

Our ship rolled back onto an even keel and I started to breathe again. We found out afterwards that the ship, a large cargo-passenger, was straggling at the back of a convoy homeward bound from Halifax. She had had engine trouble and was trying to catch up with the convoy, cutting a corner off the route by steaming northwards. If, as the chief engineer remarked, we had been a few hours earlier in that same spot we might have been run down by the convoy and lost a good deal more than one wing of the bridge, a thing superflous to the smooth running of the ship anyway, like its occupiers. So the chief sneered. The rivalry between engine-room and deck was as old as steam, and the chief seemed quite pleased at the inconvenience the absence of one wing of the bridge caused the deck officers.

The second mate, Mr. Chapman, who was looking out on the port side at the time of the collision, fortunately saw the dark shape looming up, shouted "Hard a-starboard!" to the man at the wheel, then flung himself into the wheelhouse just as the paravane boom began to shear away the portion of the bridge from under his feet.

When I went into the galley after the excitement had died down, the bos'n was in there warming his thick hands, and grinning hugely, malignantly, out of a khaki balaclava.

"What did I tell yer? It'll be 'er bleedin' back next. You mark my words. That was just a taster. You'll see. She'll do 'er dash yet," he prophesied.

"Aw turn it up for Christ's sake, Bose," said the cook, stirring some thick cocoa with one hand and stroking Sleet with the other.

Next morning we cleared the Newfoundland fog banks and sailed past the coast of Nova Scotia in the lemon light of winter sunshine, brittle air, and smooth, grey-green waters. The galley wireless crackled with news; we should have at least a month in port while the bridge was being repaired; the second mate was cursing like hell because he wouldn't be home in time for the birth of his first child; one of the seamen was planning to jump ship and get a job on a ranch; The Count was scheming to fly to New York to see one of his judies; the deucer—second engineer—hated the idea of wasting time in port when the filthy Germans were still swarming all over his country. Everybody else was well pleased with the idea of being in the States for repairs.

We considered ourselves safely in American territorial waters now, patrolled by the U.S. Navy, though we never saw any of their patrol boats. For the next few days we coasted southwards and one evening I saw a glow in the sky which puzzled me because I knew it couldn't be the Aurora Borealis as we were too far south. Moreover, the lights were to westward, and, *a fortiori,* I'd seen the Northern Lights and they didn't look as static as this, nor as monochromatic. This was like the glow of a car's headlamps as it nears the brow of a hill, only a thousand times bigger. I asked the Fiver about the phenomenon when he came on deck.

"Those are the lights of New York City. We're only about fifty miles off Long Island," he said.

"Do you mean to say that the glow from the lights can be seen fifty miles away?" I asked incredulously.

"Aye," answered the sometimes laconic Fiver.

He was right, so right that later, when the Americans came into the war, New York's lighting had to be reduced as it was discovered that even fifty miles away allied ships were silhouetted and made easy targets for U-boats prowling in that area.

Three days after seeing the lights, making a total of eighteen days out from Liverpool, we steamed slowly up the quiet Chesapeake Bay and moored alongside an oiling wharf just across the water from our destined port. Big notices read : NO NAKED LIGHTS. Matches had been struck on them. We tanked up with fuel and next morning bustling tugs moved us across to our allotted berth in the East Falls Docks.

We were now in Baltimore itself.

V

As soon as the s.s. *Vesta* was tied up and the gangway in place, the ship swarmed with American government officials, custom's officers, coast-guards, busybodies, dock police, British Consular representatives, two padres from the local mission and a host of leisurely dock-workers and stevedores dressed in clean blue jeans. They looked like a crowd of civil servants going square-dancing. Each carried a little metal box containing his lunch, and almost as soon as they had come aboard a whistle shrilled somewhere in the nearby dockland. As one man they all sat down, opened their little black boxes and took out sandwiches wrapped in cellophane and packed in paper napkins. They held the sandwiches with the napkins while they ate them.

"Wonder what a Liverpool or Glasgow docker would think about this lot?" murmured the Fiver beside me.

"All very right and proper, though," I reminded him.

"Yes, but I can't help feeling that in this country cleanliness isn't merely *next* to Godliness : it *is* Godliness."

"Well, after all, Hygieia was one of Athena's titles, and . . ." I began, reaching back into what seemed a half-forgotten world of learning, but stopped as two burly bluejackets came towards us wearing caps on which said on them : U.S COASTGUARD.

"Either of you two the ship's gunner?" the bigger of the two asked.

"Guilty," said I.

"Royal Navy?" asked his mate, and seeing me nod my head, added, "Then I guess we could arrest you."

He nudged the other. He had a large pasty face and wore steel-rimmed glasses and had probably never been outside American territorial waters—if to sea at all.

"What for?" I asked.

"Just for bein' here, that's what for," he answered. "You're a member of the armed forces of a belligerent nation, and we don't have to harbour guys like you. We could kick you outa here in twenty-four hours—if we weren't big-hearted."

He shifted his gum, nudged his companion and winked. This obvious leg pulling with a dead-pan expression may have been an accepted form of American humour, but it annoyed me coming from someone who looked less like a seaman than the average labour-exchange clerk. I decided to call their bluff.

"Perhaps you'd like to see the captain about it," I said. "Follow me."

I started off along the flying-bridge, but the two sailors leapt forward and the bigger one barred my way.

"Here, hold on," he said uneasily, "we were jus' kiddin'. Show us your powder room now, there's a good fellah."

"My what?"

"Where you keep the ammunition," interpreted the other.

"Oh, you mean the magazine? This way then," I said, leading them farther aft.

"Ain't them things you read?" muttered the big one, lumbering along the deck.

We were clambering over the barriers of our common language. I showed them the mag., the guns and ready-use lockers to satisfy them that everything explosive had been stowed away and locked up. To ascertain this was apparently the purpose of their visit. As they took their leave the big one said :

"Well, so long. We're rootin' for yer."

"It didn't seem like it," I answered.

"Aw shucks, just kidding," said the pasty one.

They gangled off. I wondered idly if playing baseball made

them walk like that. I didn't see how it could, so lost for an alternative explanation I shrugged the matter off and went below to the mess. One of the padres was trying to revive religion in Colin, but wasn't getting very far because he couldn't understand a word the mess-boy said, except "Presbyterian." I managed to creep into my cabin unnoticed but daren't close the door in case it attracted the sin-bos'n's attention. On my chest of drawers someone had put an ash-tray in the form of a Hitler effigy about six inches tall. It was like a miniature totem pole and the base, to receive ash and rest a cigarette, was roughtly heart-shaped. Amused, and thinking perhaps it was an advertisement, I picked the object up and turned it over. It now appeared to be a priapus and the base resembled testacles—another form of American humour, but more appreciated this time. Chuckling, I put the thing back on the drawers. I guessed the Fiver had got it from somewhere and had left it in my cabin for a joke. This was right. He had bought it from one of the stevedores who apparently made such *objets d'art* out of plaster-of-paris in his spare time, and sold them furtively, particularly on ships.

The padre, having failed to re-Christianize Colin, saw me in the cabin and decided that I might be an easier victim, so he came forward and stepped inside without ceremony or invitation.

I snatched up the phallic ornament and held it behind my back.

"Well, hello son! Welcome to the United States of America! Here's a big hand for you," he boomed, positively radiating Patriotism, Good Fellowship and Zeal.

He held out the big hand. I took it, and shook it, an odd sensation as there was no power in his grip. It was like shaking somebody's foot. For some moments he embarrassed me with quaintly phrased religious questions, then he thrust a leaflet into my hand and waved good-bye, saying:

"And the address of our meeting-place is on there. Come right over some night and let your hair down in God's presence!"

He went. I relaxed and put the Hitler-priapus back on the drawers, then on second thoughts I put it *in* one of the drawers, just in case my cabin should be invaded by any more revivalists. I glanced at the pamphlet still in my hand. On it was a picture of an elderly, bearded gentleman with his forefinger in a point-blank Kitchener attitude and a speech-balloon emanating from his mouth in which were the words : I WANT YOU, SON.

After some consideration I decided that this smiling old gent was not Uncle Sam after all, but God. He wasn't wearing Uncle Sam's traditional striped trousers and star-spangled top hat. While I was musing thus on the comic-strip approach to anthropomorphism, two much more businesslike naval men that the coast-guards I had met came into the mess. This was what would nowa-days be called a screening party. One of the men was a lieut-enant, the other a petty officer. They rounded up all the engin-eers, as well as Colin and myself, and questioned us about various things : had we been to the States before; if so, for how long; when, why, wherefore? My turn came and I stood before the two seated men feeling like the boy who was asked when he last saw his father.

"Ever been in the United States or her territories, previous to this visit?" the lieutenant asked.

I replied that I had not.

"Ever been deported from any country at all?" he next asked.

"No," I said. "Certainly not."

"All right, no need to get British about it!" the petty officer snapped.

Up jumped the chief engineer.

"Mind your manners, young man! We're all British here, ex-cept for the second, and we're fighting a war that you may well be in yoursel' afore long."

He sat down suddenly and glared at the Americans. We waited tensely for the riposte.

"Huh," grunted the P.O., and we all relaxed.

The lieutenant pushed his cap back on his forehead and smiled lazily.

"He got you there, Joe," he said mildly to the petty officer, "Now shut up, there's a good fellah."

To me he said :

"These are just routine questions, son. Nothing personal in them at all."

He was very pleasant and told me that although I was a Royal Navy man I was free to move about anywhere on shore in civilian clothes, but that I was not officially—he italicized "officially"—supposed to sleep ashore, owing to the fact that I was a member of the armed forces of a belligerent nation. He then winked and handed me my shore pass.

"Next," he said.

I took the wink to mean : but you ain't armed now, and you don't look very belligerent, and a guy's gotta sleep somewhere, so what the hell?

Colin sidled up to me and whispered hoarsely :

"The Old Man wants you on the bridge."

When I arrived on the bridge the captain was in an anxiety state. He told me that I'd better put the firing locks of the guns immediately in the magazine as he'd just been informed that one

had been stolen from the last British ship that had put into Baltimore. Captain Eldrich then looked round furtively and said in
a low, secret-agent voice:

"There are Nazis among 'em."

Alarmed, I went swiftly to the guns, glancing suspiciously at
the clean stevedores, the big men placidly chewing gum and
making leisurely movements about the deck. I removed the locks,
stowed them in the magazine, then hid myself in the heads—
as ship's lavatories are called—where I could smoke and read a
few chapters of Anthony Trollope's *Last Chronicle of Barset*
Vol. II, a book which I'd found that day in the saloon and carried
away as loot to my cabin. I have still never read Vol. I.

So the afternoon frittered away. By tea-time the air was as
crisp as a cornflake. A star showed clear and bright in the sky
and lights began to appear in the town. A huge advertisement for
some innocent drink flashed intermittently and for the first time
I noticed a large brick building on the wharf, not more than a
ship's length away. It was not lit up and looked too respectable
to be a warehouse. Indeed, it was rather like a big noncomform-
ist chapel: the double doors looked as though they were seldom
opened and there was an indescribable gloom about the place
which filled me with irrational horror. I stopped the last of the
dockers who was just about to leave the ship and asked him what
the building was. He shifted his gum and spat casually at Sleet
who was funambulating along a handrail, missed, looked sharply
at me, and said:

"City morgue."

Then he picked up his toolbox and hurried down the gangway
as if Death were after him, while I rushed down to the mess,
chased by a running grave.

In the mess all was comparatively gay and frivolous. Even the
chief looked jolly and the Deucer seemed more relaxed than ever
I'd seen him before. At six o'clock we all trooped to the saloon to
draw some pay. It made me a little envious to watch the merchant
seamen "subbing" forty or fifty dollars against their comparatively
big wages, when I dare sub only fifteen against mine. But then, I
remembered, I was only a passenger. The mate had told me that
there was no need to keep watches while the ship was in Baltimore
as there would always be a policeman on board doing an anti-
sabotage watch. This meant that I had plenty of leisure—too
much in fact for the small amount of money I had to spend. I
saw myself dimeless after about a week, haunting art galleries,
wandering around museums and staring at monuments, perhaps
even letting my hair down in God's Presence with the hearty mis-
sionary.

Dimeless after a week? The very next morning I had exactly one dollar! This was the reason. When I had drawn my pay I went back to the cabin to spruce up my civilian suit which was badly creased. I was rushing back and forth from cabin to pantry with a hot iron trying vainly to produce a knife-edged pair of trousers, when the Count appeared. He was immaculate. His uniform fitted him perfectly; his moustache was neatly trimmed; his shoes like mirrors. He looked unreal. He also looked horrified.

"You're not," he choked, "you're not thinking of going ashore in that working suit, are you?"

"Believe it or not," I answered, "but these are the only clothes I have—apart from uniforms, which I'm not allowed to wear ashore. Besides, I didn't know you were coming with us on this 'run' to-night. I thought you were going to New York?"

"Not until next week, so I thought to-night would be as good as any to give you the benefit of my wide experience of life—in other words, to show you the town."

"You've been here before, then?" I asked.

The Count made an airy gesture.

"No, but they're all the same, once you know the ropes," he said "Oh, I see," I said dubiously. "Well, I won't be long."

Soon the Count, the Fiver, the third engineer and I went ashore. The third with his corgi temperament, from the disrespectful way in which he approached people, especially policemen, would run us into trouble before the night was out, I felt sure.

Baltimore's traffic startled me at first. The cars were bigger and faster than ours and it amazed me that there wasn't an accident at every corner. It was wonderful to walk down well-lighted streets, after the blacked-out cities at home. As we strolled along East Baltimore Street sniffing like dogs the strange, exciting new smells, it struck me how representative of the United Kingdom we were : the Count was Irish, the Fiver a Scotsman, the third engineer Welsh, and I was the Englishman. We were a walking traditional anecdote, we four in the streets of America.

It was quite early, about seven o'clock, when we entered without knowing it a district known as The Block. It was Baltimore's Barbary Coast, a region full of night clubs which simply looked like small cafés with easy names : Joe's Place, Galley Bar, Kate's, Charlie's, Sam's, and other tough, terse titles. In this district also were the small theatres where the girlie-shows, leg-shows, tit-shows or Burlesque took place. The natives pronounced it "Burlecue," by analogy with barbecue, I supposed.

"What about a cup of coffee before we start the fun?" the Count suggested in unnecessarily loud tones to attract the attention of some passing citizens.

"You're not thinking of going into one of these places for coffee?" I said.

The Count looked at me scornfully and said in a louder voice with an exaggerated English accent:

"And why not? They're all perfectly respectable—at this early hour."

"I wasn't thinking of their morals, but simply doubting that they sold anything so innocuous as coffee," I answered, maddened by the Count's superior tones and ludicrous affectations.

"Ah, but we know they do, don't we, Third?" the Count said, turning to the Welshman who scowled at him for his pains and muttered cryptically:

"Maybe we do, and maybe we don't."

"Och, well, let's try this one," said the Fiver, pointing to a small place which was not more pretentious in appearance than any of the dozen of delicatessens with which the port seemed to abound.

We agreed. The place looked innocent enough for coffee. Quiet, friendly, it glowed with warm lights and just inside the door was a small cocktail bar, but this did not open until eight. We went inside; a barman in shirtsleeves pottered behind the counter.

"All we got is coffee and coke—in there," he jerked a square thumb towards a curtain. "Too early for real drinks," he added apologetically.

As we moved towards the café department we passed a door on which was written the simple phrase, THE BOSS, in gold letters four inches high. Terse, these Americans, I thought.

"Is 'coke' short for cocoa?" I asked the Fiver.

"Ah hope not. I didna come all this way to drink that muck," he grunted.

The club-café was quite deserted. There were about a dozen tables arranged in a half-circle around a tiny dance floor, at the other side of which was a raised platform—the bandstand, presumably. We sat and smoked at a table not far from the entrance. Presently a girl appeared and asked for our order. It was impossible to have just coffee. You had to have sandwiches, or some other snack, and coffee, she said.

"But we're not hungry," I protested.

The girl bit the end of her pencil and grinned.

"You don't have to eat the sandwiches—just have to pay for them," she said amiably.

With an expansive gesture the Count took command of the situation.

"Well, that's fair enough," he said in a loud voice. "Four coffees *and* sandwiches, if you please, me darlin'."

He smiled winningly at the girl who knew she had already won.

After she had gone he beamed magnanimously at us and
said :

"This is on me, gentlemen."

The Fiver kicked me lightly underneath the table.

"Wait till he gets the bill," he said softly.

Four coffees and four rounds of papery sandwiches cost the
Count nearly eighteen shillings, in American money, of course.
A woman appeared from nowhere and with a studied, or rather
practised casualness asked the third for a light. He snapped a
lighter in her face. She was about forty, but debauched beyond
her years. Her face was covered with thick powder to mask the
bags and wrinkles, sags and crinkles. She noticed the open tin
of Player's which the Count in his largess had left on the table.

"Oh, English cigarettes, mind if I have one? Get awful sick o'
these—'specially after four or five packs a day," she said, tossing
a packet of Lucky Strike onto the table.

The Count gallantly offered her all the cigarettes, and his
chair, but she declined, took one cigarette and said :

"Got a chair coming up, honey."

Sure enough, the barman was immediately behind her with a
chair from one of the other tables. The woman, who introduced
herself as Marguerita, sat down between the Count and myself
and began to talk. It was easy, pleasant patter at first, but soon
she began to gush about the British and this made us all feel
slightly sick, except the Count who seemed to take it all in and
like it. Soon three other women had arrived and were posted
between us all by the attentive barman, so that we could neither
kick nor nudge each other but had to converse openly. This was
annoying to me because I wanted to suggest to the others that
we should move on to another place before we became too deeply
involved in this one. When the Fiver tentatively mentioned an
appointment he thought he ought to keep, the blonde girl on his
left squealed with delight.

"He says he has 'an appointment'. Ain't he cute?" she giggled
to her companions.

"Yeah, he talks kinda cute, too," agreed Marguerita.

The Fiver blushed beetroot and obviously silently vowed never
to use that expression in low company again. The club began
to fill up and I resigned myself to the fact that we were now
trapped for the evening, or to the end of our money. I heard a
voice behind me—as if in answer to a question—saying :

"Nope. I come here once a week, just to let mah hair down."

It reminded me of the mission-man. I only hoped God wasn't
present. I slewed round in my chair and glanced at the speaker waving a cigar in his pudgy fingers; a short, fat man, completely bald.

The Count was now neglecting Marguerita and turning his attention towards the younger, more attractive girl between him and the Third Engineer. Her professional name was Pauline, a blonde with honey skin and big blue eyes full of meaningless expression. I inched my chair away from the older woman next to me every time she was looking in another direction, but professional hostesses are not so easily put off, especially the experienced ones, and Marguerita was an experienced one. Big of hip and bosom, in some other setting she might have been called matronly. Her conversation was animated but artificial. But then, she was in an artificial business, listening and talking to bores at ten per cent commission on everything they ate or drank.

"Do you work here every night?" I asked during a break in her patter.

She looked at me with glazed eyes.

"Six nights. On the seventh I rest from my labours, take in a movie or something," she sighed.

I wondered about the labours.

"Say, you're rather cute," she said quickly, perhaps thinking her professional talk was getting below standard and that I wasn't receiving my money's worth of flattery, sycophancy and feminine attention, "What's your name?"

"Henry," I replied, bravely.

She repeated the name softly, three times, in an incantatory manner, half to herself, as if it were a charm against the stitch or a sudden pregnancy. I jumped as she leaned forward and put her hand affectionately on mine.

"Well, Henry," she said in a voice fractured with alcoholic emotion and her eyes full of original sin, "buy us a drink, huh?"

I signalled to a cruising waitress. The drinks had a rum basis and were served in tiny tub glasses. They were very expensive and a round of eight of these, which my hostess had thoughtfully ordered, dwindled my dollars considerably. Later in the evening she again pressed my hand affectionately and in a moving voice asked if she might order a sandwich for herself as she was *dying* of hunger. I readily agreed. After all, a sandwich couldn't cost very much, not just one, even here. But once again I hadn't reckoned on my hostess' thoughtfulness. Sandwiches for eight people, together with an exotic salad and olives, followed by a *soufflé* and ice-cream—a curious meal if ever there was one—left me, after tipping the waitress, with exactly one dollar. I was determined not to part with that. The rest of the evening would have to be at someone else's expense.

At about nine o'clock a five-piece negro band darkened the dais and began to play a hot number entitled, *Wadda you know,*

Joe? Joseph it appeared, was a singularly uninformed person who knew, in fact, nothing. The response made this quite clear, partly by repetition :

> *Wadda you know, Joe?*
> *Ah don't know nothin'.*
> *Wadda you know, Joe?*
> *Ah don't know nothin'.*
> *Wadda you know, Joe?*
> *Ah don't know nothin'.*

There may have been other words but these were certainly the most insistent.

We were all startled when we discovered that our hostesses were also entertainers. Suddenly one put down her cigarette and walked over to the dais, there to sing a torch song full of self-pity, usually on the theme of unrequited love. But my big shock came when Marguerita stood up and started to take her clothes off to the rhythm of lecherous music played by the negroes. It was only half a strip-tease act really, the laws of Baltimore forbidding nudity in night clubs. So Marguerita contented herself, though not the customers, by stripping down to a huge brassière which hammocked her big breasts, and a pair of voluminous drawers— presumably the sort the male customers saw their mothers in when they were little boys, But no, this was too subtle. The tent-like garment was probably a regulation size, stipulated by the local vigilance committee. The audience clapped, whistled and cheered enthusiastically as the woman danced about the floor in these re-volting bloomers, with swaying hips and swinging tits, finally dis-appearing, to my immense relief, through a doorway next to the bandstand. I realized afterwards that seen on the stage the act might have made me laugh, but I found it embarrassing in such a confined space. The Count and the third were cheering as wildly as the rest, but the Fiver was looking as uncomfortable as I felt. The bald fat man got up and tried to run after Marguerita, but tripped over somebody's deliberately outstretched foot and meas-ured his short length on the slippery floor.

Later in the evening, when Marguerita had rejoined us— fully dressed—we had another "snack," at the third's expense this time. The meal was a repetition of the first, as his hostess had asked for a sandwich too, it seemed.

By midnight the Fiver and I could stand it no longer. I felt ill with smoking and eating too much, besides drinking the cheap liquor which had been dear to buy and foul to drink, and far from making me drunk had sobered me depressingly. I longed for my fourteen dollars back as my imagination presented me with sad pictures of myself sitting in the heads of the old *Vesta,* reading *The Last Chronicle of Barset,* Vol. II for the remainder of our stay in port.

The Fiver and I decided to make a bolt for the exit while our two hostesses had gone off to "freshen themselves," as they put it. We said farewell to the Count and the third who were hanging on in hopes of further entertainment at the girls' apartments after the club had closed at 2 a.m. They were unlucky, as we heard the next day, for the girls slipped out of a side door and into a waiting taxi—this was part of their nightly routine—while the two men sat smoking in the club until they were finally ejected by the bouncer, an enormous negro ex-boxer I had seen filling the doorway once or twice earlier in the evening. The third had made the mistake of squaring up to the dark giant when asked to leave, and trying to punch him on the chin. The blow fell short by about three feet and the third never had the chance to try another. He and the Count were picked up and dropped outside onto the pavement, like two cats being put out for the night. A passing policeman had remarked mildly :

"Don't forget your hats, boys."

VI

NEXT MORNING I watched repair work being carried out on the bridge wing. I was feeling annoyed with myself over the previous night's prodigality and even the thought that others had come off worse than myself didn't cheer me. The Count and the third had probably been slung out of dumps, dens, and dives in every big seaport in the world—and some of the smaller ones—but they didn't learn. It would happen to them again, and again, and again. Perhaps they didn't want to learn. Perhaps I was being priggish. Anyway, the Count was now unable to go to New York as he had spent the fare; the third was sulking in his cabin and would probably be there for a few days. The Fiver had been granted a few days' leave to visit an aunt in Philadelphia and had left early on a luxurious long distance bus. Mr. Campbell had disappeared as soon as the ship had docked and hadn't been heard of since. Two of the seamen, Johnston and Harris, were in jail for being fighting drunk.

I leaned on the rail and stared gloomily at the city morgue. It stared back at me with its dead window eyes. If I go ashore again, I thought, I'll go alone. I fingered my one dollar bill then took it out of my pocket and looked at it. It looked unreal, like stage money, not like English money at all. English money? I suddenly remembered that I had two English pound notes stuffed in the purse of my belt in the cabin! Could I change them anywhere? If I could it meant a pleasant run ashore that same evening, perhaps a theatre, certainly a decent meal.

After I had shaved and changed I went to see the third mate. He told me that the British consul had consented to change English pounds for members of the crew at the high rate of four dollars forty cents. This was forty cents higher than the current bank rate. The consul kept a swank restaurant in the city, but whether the consulship or the restaurant was the sideline the third mate didn't know. I didn't care, but made for the place at top speed.

The Britannia Restaurant was situated in the busiest part of the town and obviously caught a wealthy business clientele. One entrance to the restaurant was through the bar, the long counter of which was lined with lager-drinking enemy agents, each with a foot on the brass rail, all smoking under low brimmed hats and regarding me cleverly in the mirror behind the bar as I passed by. A barman was wiping glasses and I asked him if I could see the consul.

"What's your business?" he grunted.

"My own."

"Got an appointment?"

"No."

He leaned forward urgently.

"You from the British ship?" he whispered.

"Yes."

"Okay. See what I can do."

He disappeared through the restaurant doorway and I bought myself a lager to toy with till he came back. He soon returned with a small hurrying man in gold-rimmed glasses who looked at me sharply.

"Are you a British seaman?" he asked in low tones.

"Yes."

"What ship?"

I thought this a silly question as ours was the only British ship in the port and he had been aboard only the previous day. Someone had pointed him out to me as the consul's secretary. But I told him the ship's name. He gave me a look which I found difficult to interpret, and did a loud cough which drowned the name of "*Vesta*".

"Caught you there," he said. "You shouldn't have disclosed the name of your ship, you know. I might not have been the person you thought I was."

He looked furtively up and down the long bar at the reflected enemy agents pretending to be smoking, drinking, reading newspapers but really cleverly regarding *our* reflections in the long mirror.

"But that's ridiculous," I protested. "The name of the ship is painted on a board which is hung on the bridge. Anybody can walk in and out of the docks. There aren't even any dock gates. And as for not knowing who you are, I saw you yesterday when you came aboard with the consul."

He held up a small, sharp finger, warningly.

"All the same, you can't be too careful," he said. "Now, what is it you want?"

I pulled the two pound notes out of my pocket.

"I'd like these changed, please," I answered hopefully.

Anyone would think I'd flashed a couple of stolen diamonds.

"Put them away at once!" the secretary hissed. "Yes, we'll change them. The barman will arrange it. Have a drink on the house. Good day and—be careful!"

I thanked him and put the money guiltily in my pocket. He hurried back into the restaurant as if his ice-cream were going cold.

"What'll it be?" the barman asked.

"What have you got, besides nursery drinks?" I said in a tough, seadoggy manner, contemptuously shoving the lager glass aside.

"Shot o' Scotch?" the barman suggested.

"Make it Irish," I said, perversely.

Had it been Welsh whisky, I wouldn't have known the difference. The barman poured me the drink and passed it along the counter, together with eight dollars and eighty cents. He also slid a napkin towards me.

"Put the Limey dough under that and shove it back," he said under his breath.

I did as I was bid and put a twenty-five cent piece on top, wondering whether this was enough, or too much to tip the man for his service.

"Thanks, Jack," he grinned, flipping the coin into the air and catching it cleverly in his coat pocket by holding it open, a bar trick he must have practised hundreds of times to achieve such perfection.

Having declined both soda and plain water for my whisky, I was now obliged to toss it down at a gulp in front of the barman —just to show that I was no sea puppy. A fire seemed to have been suddenly started deep down inside me. Flames, or at any rate, fumes poured out of my nostrils. I gripped the counter for support with one hand and with the other pretended to blow my nose. I was really coughing into it. Fortunately the barman was now serving someone else, a big man in a Norfolk jacket, a little way down the bar. When I had recovered I smoked and idly watched expensive secretaries going in to lunch with their sugar-bosses. I felt hungry, but was sure that food in this place would cost a dollar a bite, so I left and found a Chinese restaurant down a side street. There I got a hillock of chop-suey for eighty five cents, half of which I had to leave, but not before I had extracted all the chicken bits from it. As I sat smoking and drinking milkless China tea I wondered where the saloon was in which Edgar Allan Poe had collapsed and died. Doubtless it no longer existed. Then I remembered that W. H. Davies had often mentioned Baltimore in his *Autobiography of A Super Tramp*. He had embarked for Liverpool by cattle-boat from this port several times, but before doing so had often to beg his food and lodgings until a cattleman's job was vacant on one of the ships. He always found the people of Baltimore generous and charitable, he said. One of his waiting passage jobs was oyster fishing in Chesapeake Bay, but this turned out to be unprofitable except for the captains of the fishing vessels.

As it was late there was only one other customer for lunch in the little restaurant. He was sitting near the window, a big man whose face was hidden behind a copy of *The Baltimore Sun*— which he appeared to be reading. I asked the waiter, a bottle-shouldered Chinese, for my bill, and when he brought it the man by the window asked for his. The waiter glided silently over to him.

I left the restaurant and made for the main street, bought some cigarettes and sauntered off enjoying the strange sights and foreign smells of hamburgers, cars, cigars, and perfumed women. I turned into a bar and ordered a brand of beer I'd seen advertised somewhere. By way of making conversation I asked the bartender what time they closed.

"Three to four," he answered.

I frowned.

"Well, what time do you open?"

"I just told yer, four o'clock," he mouthed the answer round a dead cigar butt, the end of which he was chewing.

Then I noticed the sign which read: OPEN 23 OUT OF THE 24 HOURS. It was a sort of drugstore as well and the bar wasn't open for all of the twenty three hours. Still I was puzzled.

"But why bother to shut for just the odd hour?" I persisted.

The barman grinned and showed a number of brown, broken teeth which went well with his cauliflower ears and battered nose.

"Gotta get some sleep sometime, mister," he said.

It was five to three. A big man was leaning up against the far end of the counter reading *The Baltimore Sun*. I recognized the Norfolk jacket, heavy, loosely woven like a bird's nest. It was the same I had seen in the bar of The Britannia when I was buying dollars, and in the chop-suey place, now I came to think about it.

The beer tasted like flat mineral water. I finished it off, however, and went wonderingly back into the street. I lit a cigarette and looked back slyly. The man was looking in a shop window one block away. I moved on and so did he. I went into Woolworth's and bought a toothbrush I didn't really want. The man was at another counter buying something he didn't really want. If he was an enemy agent he wasn't a very good one, I decided. Surely it would have been better to employ small, inconspicuous men who could move unobtrusively instead of this great mountain of tweed, this six-foot-four college athlete type? But had I really fallen among spies? A fantasy presented itself to my mind : as I walked along the pavement a large dark car drew up alongside me, the door opened and I was bundled into the back seat by the big man who got in after me and pressed the muzzle of a Lüger into my ribs. He growls out an order in a foreign tongue—German—to the other agent who is already sitting in the back of the car and pressing the muzzle of another Lüger into my other ribs, as we drive smoothly and silently away.

The vision passed and I found myself staring at some sanitary towels disguised as brown paper parcels. Momentarily embarrassed, I hurried out into the street clutching my new toothbrush. Doubling my tracks, I set off up the street, determined to stop the first policeman I met and tell him about the man who was shadowing me. This does not sound very heroic, but then he was a very big man and he was still following me as I observed by pausing and pretending to tie my shoelace.

There was a policeman directing traffic in the middle of the crossroads some distance ahead. I led my pursuer up the street until we were about level with the traffic cop, then I turned sharply and crossed to the middle of the road. A car had to brake suddenly to avoid running me down. The policeman glared and confronted me with hands on hips.

"Looking for an undertaker, son?" he growled.

I ignored the remark and hurriedly told him that I was a British seaman and that a suspicious character was following me around the town and had been doing so for most of the afternoon. I pointed the man out, now striding quickly up the street. The cop said :

"That him, the big fellah?"

I nodded. He waved some traffic on, unconcernedly.

"Probably a fairy," he said, looking down and grinning at me in a worldly fashion.

A fairy? The American slang word for a homosexual was new

to me, at least, this one was. However, one quickly learns such things. Although he was big, the man did look a bit soft, now I came to think about it. I thanked the traffic cop and went away, biting my lips with rage. When I arrived back on board the *Vesta* I snarled at Colin as everybody else did, then I cooled down and, conscience-stricken, apologized to him.

After tea I went on deck and smoked against the ship's rail, staring down at the city morgue. The tide was high and the quay seemed far below. I didn't notice the youth in a trilby and raglan until he hailed me from the wharf :

"What ship is this?"

His voice sounded clear, but distant.

"*Vesta*," I shouted down through cupped hands, then I spat, seamanlike, over the side, but not near him.

I wondered why the youth hadn't seen the ship's name on the board hanging from the bridge.

"Where from?" came the voice again.

"England," I answered and again, spat.

He shouted something else which I couldn't quite hear, so I decided to go down and talk to him. His voice sounded pleasantly boyish and I needed to talk big to somebody little just then.

When I reached the foot of the gangway he walked to meet me. Though only about seventeen he was as tall as myself. I ignored him and walked towards the after moorings, then I tested them with my foot in a seamanlike manner, as though I had come down the gangway especially for this purpose. He strolled towards the bollard where I stood.

"Hiya," he said.

His trilby was tilted slightly back and his raglan was undone. He looked like a film version of a cub reporter, as no doubt he intended to look. I liked him at once. He had clear grey eyes set wide apart, high cheekbones and square, even teeth. He looked honest and intelligent and not without a sharp sense of humour. I remember thinking vaguely that if I'd had a younger brother I should have liked him to be like this, and not have to go to wars.

"Hello," I said. "Not thinking of running away to sea, are you?"

He smiled.

"No, not really. I often come down to look at the ships though. You see, I'm bored with my job."

"What sort of job is it?" I asked.

He looked gloomy.

"I'm a radio salesman in a big store. I'm interested in radio, but——"

"Not in selling it?" I cut in.

"Right. I want to get a job in a studio."

He said "stoodio." I rolled a seamanlike cigarette while he watched, fascinated.

"This is the first British ship I've ever seen," he said suddenly, looking wondrously at the old *Vesta,* as if she were an ocean queen or the *K.G. V.* "And you're the first British seaman I've ever met. Mind if I shake your hand?"

I didn't mind. Americans always seemed to want to shake hands —and swop names.

"I'm Jimmy—Donchenko," he added the surname as if it were an afterthought.

"Henry Warren," I said as we shook hands.

"That sounds very English," he commented.

"Yours sounds very Russian—at least the second half does." He sighed.

"Yeah. I get ribbed about it daily. The boss calls me 'The Siberian'. My folks came over from the Ukraine. I'm what the sociologists term a 'first generation American.' You must meet my folks. How about coming up to dinner, to-night?"

"I'd like to very much. But won't they mind?"

"I'll phone 'em and find out," he said frankly. "There's a telephone at the end of the wharf."

We walked together up the quay and into the busy street. The Telephone was just inside the doorway of the general store and Jimmy Donchenko dialled his home number. I stood off at a polite distance, but I might have saved my manners. He spoke in Russian. After what seemed a lengthy conversation he rang off and turned to me.

"Mom says it'll be O.K. Six o'clock. I have to go uptown to buy some things, but I'll be back and pick you up at a quarter of six," he said.

I thanked him.

"Oh, by the way, don't bother to doll up. It'll be a very informal dinner you know. in the kitchen."

We parted company. I went back to the ship to clean, if not to doll myself up.

As I polished my shoes a doubt clouded the clear and pleasant image I had in mind of the young Donchenko. The Russians were not yet in the war. Nobody knew whose side they would be on if they did come into it. Suppose they had an anti-British spy system at work in the States? Suppose this Donchenko boy were a Red and not a White? But then surely he wouldn't be using a Russian name at all, and certainly not talking Russian into public telephones—unless he were covering his guile with frankness? No. Too subtle.

I finished cleaning my shoes, washed and went up to the galley
for a yarn. Besides, Jimmy Donchenko was too young to be a spy.
An apprentice, then? Nonsense.

"She'll break 'er bleedin' back 'omeward bound, you'll see,"
the bos'n's voice of doom cut through the galley's fug and bit into
my brain. The words hung there.

Was I walking into a Bolshevik trap? I saw myself strapped to
a chair, musk-rats nibbling at my feet encouraged by big whis-
kered Bolshies in top boots, laughing and burning my chest with
their cheap cigars, while I sat as silent and not-telling as a Duk-
hobor.

The sound of a car's horn shook off these fantasies and the
watchman who had just come off duty poked his head in the
galley and said that somebody was asking for somebody called
Warren. I left the galley and made my way down the plank.
There was apprentice-spy Donchenko sitting in a large taxi, waiting to deliver me into the hands of his confederates.

The taxi took us at seat-gripping speed to a quiet district and
we stopped at a house in a terrace. There were gardens in front
of the houses, but there were no gates or fences, just low box
hedges dividing each garden from its neighbour.

"Home," said Jimmy.

He paid the driver, then taking my arm confidentially as we
went up the path to the house, said :

"I don't usually smoke in the house. You don't mind, do you?"

I supposed he meant would I mind not smoking in the house
either, so I agreed not to.

Uniformly dull outside, the house indoors was interesting with
its fusion of Russian and American cultures. It was predomin-
antly American in furnishings. The reception room was spacious
and thickly-carpeted. An ikon stood enshrined in one corner. It
was in triptych form and rested on a small table. In another corner was a big radiogram, while a samovar adorned the sideboard.
A grand piano was visible through the open doorway of the
drawing-room, and resting on top of it was a stringed instrument
I fancied was a balalaika, though I'd never seen a balalaika before and wasn't sure what one looked like.

"Who are the family music makers?" I asked.

"My sisters," said Jimmy, throwing his coat off. "Come down
and meet them."

"Down?"

"Yes, down in the kitchen," he answered, tossing his trilby
onto a hatstand peg. "We always eat down there in winter. It's
warmer."

He led the way down a staircase to a brilliantly-lighted kitchen.

It seemed to be full of people, obviously waiting for us before beginning their meal. At the head of the table sat an old monumental woman with a thick, goitrous neck.

"Grandma," said Jimmy, "doesn't speak English."

Grandma smiled and inclined her head with a not ungracious movement. I gathered that she had been informed of my coming. I shook hands with Jimmy's parents, to whom he next introduced me. The father was a quiet, bespectacled man, short, but sturdy; the mother a younger version of Grandma, whose daughter she was. She spoke English, however, though with a strong accent, and she was very affable. Only one thing bothered me about her: she would giggle at things I said which weren't supposed to be funny. Perhaps it was *my* accent which aroused her mirth, as she had apparently never met an Englishman before, or perhaps it was something to do with the Ukrainian sense of humour. It was certainly alarming at times.

Jimmy's brother was a dark-haired, serious man of twenty-five. He was an aeronautical engineer and was employed at a factory on the outskirts of Baltimore. Two of his sisters were present: Anna, recently married but whose husband was out of town for a few days, and Katrina, her twin. They were twenty-three and both pleasant, good-looking girls. The third and youngest girl, Daria, had not yet come down.

"Dolling herself up for a dramatic, last-minute entry," commented Jimmy.

"James!" Mrs. Donchenko rounded on him.

Jimmy shrank. Mr. Donchenko stoked the huge boiler which heated the entire house and gave off a pleasant, unoppressive warmth in the kitchen. It struck me as odd that the girls had Russian names but the boys, James and Ronald, had not. I said so.

"Grandma chose our names," explained Katrina.

"And mother the boys," said Anna.

"It was—what you call it?—a compromise," added Mrs. Donchenko.

She was not an educated woman, nor was her husband an educated man. He had some unskilled job at the docks. They were of peasant stock, but vigorous, go-ahead. They had managed to give their five American-born children either high school or college educations. They had the house, with its standard American fittings (radios, refrigerator, good central heating system) and a car each. This must be an example of the American Way of Life, materially anyhow.

I heard footsteps coming downstairs and looked up. A tall beautiful girl entered the room and came forward to meet me.

"Daria," said Jimmy, standing up, "this is Henry."

We shook hands.

"Welcome to our country," Daria said, smiling.

It was the first time I really had felt welcome. I muttered something and gulped, realizing that all the family's eyes were upon us. I let go of Daria's hand suddenly. Mrs. Donchenko said something in Russian, then she and Grandma giggled. Confused, I sat down at the table opposite Daria and stared at my soup. It was borstch. Unknowingly my bowed attitude was appropriate, for immediately Grandma began to intone grace. The benediction seemed interminable in the unfamiliar tongue, and once I raised my eyes to look at Daria. Her head was reverently bowed and her eyes seemed to be closed. Even thus her beauty was overpowering to me. She had the high cheekbones characteristic of the Donchenkos, but apart from the grey eyes set wide apart, like Jimmy's, she was unlike the family : fair where they were dark, tall and slender where they were inclined to stockiness. Grace ended, she raised her head and her cool grey eyes rested on me for an instant. I noticed the triangular pattern of her face which was the basis of its symmetrical beauty. Jimmy gave me a keen, swift glance.

"Told you it would be a dramatic entry," he said mischievously.

"What was that, James?" Daria turned her eyes in his direction.

"Oh, nothing. Just nothing," he said, eyes innocently upturned.

"How do you like the girls in Baltimore?" Mrs. Donchenko asked, looking sidewise down the table.

"I—er—oh, splendid!" I managed to blurt out.

Katrina and Anna exchanged looks and laughed with obvious pleasure, but Daria appeared not to have heard my answer.

Throughout the dinner Mr. Donchenko said not a word, and as soon as he had finished he excused himself, got up, and presumably went out, for I didn't see him again that evening. Ronald attempted to talk about British and American aero engines to me, but saw that I had no technical knowledge and was sensitive enough to know that such a conversation would be one-sided, so gave up trying. He was no lecturer.

Daria had refused the second course, kromeskys, saying that her weight was up two pounds that week. Two pounds didn't seem very much to me.

"Does it matter?" I asked.

"It does if you're a dancer," she answered.

"Daria is a student of the ballet," explained Mrs. Donchenko, not without pride.

"Oh, that's interesting," I commented. "Full, or part-time?"

Daria didn't seem to understand so I looked at her mother; she stared back uncomprehendingly.

"I mean," I went on lamely, "do you put in a full day's work at the ballet school—or whatever it is—or do you work at something else during the day and study dancing in the evenings?"

Daria looked at me coldly.

"Dancing is not my hobby, it is my work, it is my life," she replied haughtily.

"Oh, I see," I said.

"We're very arty," Jimmy put in.

"James!" his mother said severely.

"Yes, Mom?" Jimmy answered, looking innocent and bewildered.

In a moment there began a glorious family row and it was at this point that Mr. Donchenko left us without saying good-bye— a habit of his, as I discovered later. My presence did not in the least inhibit the Donchenko's sudden acrimonious attacks on one another. Indeed, I might not have been there at all for the notice they took of me during these outbursts.

"I don't care," said Jimmy petulantly. "Daria gets all the breaks just because you think she has more talent than anybody else in the family! Look at me. I've got talent and there I am wasting it trying to sell radios all day when I should be learning all about studio production work!"

He stormed on.

"Envy is one of the Seven Sins, James," said Daria complacently, during a lull. "Work hard and some day the world will recognize and reward your talents."

She sipped her coffee. I began to wonder if she was being ironical, or if she had no sense of humour.

"May be," answered her brother, "but it just happens that I've no chance to show off my talents, even by working hard— except to my family who don't know anything about play-production anyway."

"We all thought that operetta you produced at the college last fall was wonderful," said Anna.

"Thanks, Anna," said Jimmy, somewhat mollified. "But if only I could get a job at the studios, even if it meant just a few dollars a week salary at first, then I'd show you all!"

Mrs. Donchenko looked sternly at her son, then said :

"James, we have been over this before, and you know that we cannot afford you to give up your job just yet."

Jimmy looked crestfallen. His mother softened.

"Later on perhaps, when my auto is paid for, we'll see," she said.

"Is that a promise?" exclaimed the boy excitedly.

"Yes. It is a promise, but now I think you should apologize to Daria."

Jimmy turned to his sister.

"Sure. I'm sorry, Daria. I didn't mean it. You go ahead and be the best since Pavlova."

"Thank you, James. I will try," she answered solemnly.

While this curious conversation had ensued, Grandma had been sitting with her head on one side and a puzzled, doggy expression on her face. After it was over she appeared to demand an interpretation, so her daughter obliged in rapid Russian. Then the argument, or some other argument, started up in that explosive language and everybody joined in—except me of course. I began to feel uncomfortable and wished I could smoke. Once or twice I instinctively fumbled for a cigarette, then remembering the household ban, contented myself with watching Daria's lips mouth a language I didn't understand. The language we speak, and the way we speak it must help to shape our mouths, to some extent, I mused. Suddenly Daria noticed my attention and stopped talking. I smiled self-consciously.

"I'm sorry about this." she said in a low voice. "Domestic matters. Money. You know what families are like."

Then she smiled, and I knew she was not without humour. I nodded and smiled back. Yes, I knew what families were like. Then Daria raised her voice and said in Russian something the equivalent of :

"I think we are neglecting our guest."

For at once everybody stopped talking and looked at me. There was an embarrassed silence for a few moments, then Mrs. Donchenko detailed Ronald and Katrina to do the washing up, as it was apparently their turn on the roster. The rest of us went upstairs, some to their rooms, but Daria, Jimmy and I went into the drawing-room. The telephone bell rang, for Daria. She moved with a superb grace across the room and took the instrument from Jimmy. After listening intently for a few seconds, she said :

"Ping-pong? But I don't want to play ping-pong."

More intent listening, then :

"No, nor that neither."

She replaced the instrument delicately, moved elegantly back across the room, and sat down.

"Well, what *do* you want to do?" Jimmy demanded.

Daria idly turned the pages of a magazine.

"What do you have to offer?" she asked nonchalantly.

"A drive to Washington in Mom's car, then over the Potomac

into Arlington for a steak. I know just the place—a roadhouse with nifty waitresses," exclaimed Jimmy.

"James!"

Mrs. Donchenko's voice boomed down the stairs. Jimmy gulped. "Yes, Mom?"

His mother descended with a countess air and stood glaring at the three of us.

"You are not going to use my car to go looking at waitresses —however 'nifty' they may be!" she said.

"It wasn't my idea," Daria sighed. "I don't care about nifty waitresses, though they might interest our British sailor friend."

She raised her eyebrows and gave me a long slow look over the top of her magazine. I didn't quite know how to return either the remark or the look, so I pretended to ignore them, and said as indifferently as possible:

"I'd rather like to have seen the Folger Library—though I suppose it would be closed by the time we got to Washington."

All seemed stunned. You could have heard a balalaika drop.

"The Folger Library?" Jimmy exclaimed. "Did you say the Folger Library?"

"Yes, My tutor at Oxford knows someone on the staff there. I promised to look him up if ever I came this way."

I picked up the *Saturday Evening Post* and looked at an advertisement for a pressure-cooker, without seeing it. Daria lowered her magazine.

"You were at Oxford University?" she asked.

"Yes. I took my degree there last year. Might go back and do some research after the war—if Oxford is still there after the war."

I suddenly had visions of the University being blitzed and strafed; of the Bodleian being blown to smithereens and priceless manuscripts fluttering like leaflets in the dusty air; of ancient walls crumbling and crashing to the ground; of toppling towers, steeples, pinnacles; of the unrecognizable Roman emperors round the Sheldonian nodding and shuddering, then dropping among the rest of the debris, and so finally achieving their long-sought-for anonymity; of dons hurrying for shelter, helter-skelter, holding on to their hats. *This* is the way the world would end. Not with a whimper, but with a BANG!

"And if I'm still about after the war," I added as an after-thought.

Mrs. Donchenko was suitably impressed. Her strong Cossack frame relaxed and her voice softened.

"So, you are a scholar? You did not mention this, James," she said, turning to Jimmy who was sitting open-mouthed.

"Huh?—no, I didn't—I mean, I forgot," he stammered.

"Well, James, if you think you can get Mr. Warren to Washington in one hour, perhaps this"—she hesitated, groping for the word—"this *Forger* Library will still be open, and at least Mr. Warren will be able to make inquiries about his tutor's friend."

She beamed on me.

Daria and I were in the rear seat of the comfortable Pontiac, Jimmy at the helm. He chuckled.

"Mom called it the *Forger* Library. Did you hear?"

"Don't make fun of Mother, Jimmy," Daria rebuked him.

I noticed that she dropped the formal "James" once out of the house.

"Sorry," Jimmy apologized humbly. "But that sure was a good idea of yours, Henry. All that stuff about Oxford did the trick and here we are, on our way to Washington."

He swung the purring Pontiac towards the highway which led to the capital. Daria looked at me suspiciously but I said nothing till we were past some traffic signals.

"All that stuff happens to be true," I then said to Jimmy.

"What?"

Jimmy nearly let go of the wheel. Daria's expression softened and she sank back into the depths of the corner upholstery.

"You should get to know your friends better, Jimmy," she said to her brother, then to me : "He often picks up odd people and brings them home. We're always suspicious until we get to know them."

"Then you're sometimes horrified!" laughed Jimmy.

Desperately I sought for interesting things to say to Daria, thinking that she was the sort who would despise inarticulate men. I tried Russian authors.

"I suppose you've read all the Russian classic novelists in the original?" I said, lighting a cigarette and enjoying it immensely after the prohibition.

"Most of them," she admitted.

"What about Sholokhov?" I asked, striving to think of something different to say about Russian authors.

"Only *Quiet Flows The Don*. I couldn't get on with the other."

"*Virgin Soil Upturned*? Neither could I. It's not as good of course. Lacks that wealth of telling detail which *The Don* has, but they both make a terrific impact with their realism. I suppose the second book was written to order."

"It was," affirmed Daria, then said in a different tone, "We're a Cossack family. Did you know?"

"I thought you might be, by the name. A 'chenko' ending is Cossack isn't it?"

"You are well-informed," Daria said, surprised.

I made a modest noise, but was very pleased with myself. Actually, I knew very little about the Russians and the odd fact was
just something that had lodged in my memory—possibly through
reading Sholokhov. Then I felt guilty and said :

"I don't know much about the Russians, really. I just happened
to remember about the name-ending."

"I don't know much about them either," she said, with a touch
of pride that was almost arrogance, "I'm an American."

First generation one hundred per cent American-ness, I thought.
A motor-cycle cop in leather jerkin and breeches appeared in
front of the car and flagged us down to a halt. We had just
turned onto the broad, flat highway which led to Washington.
Jimmy stopped the car and lowered the window. The big face of
a policeman looked in. He seemed like a large, friendly animal
begging for food.

"Do you mind if we have a little light on the subject?" he said
with mock-politeness.

Jimmy switched on the headlamps.

"Sorry," he said.

The cop smiled hugely.

"I hate to bother you," he said, then touched his cap to Daria
and roared away into the night.

We drove on, passing a sign which read : SPEED LIMIT 60.
Jimmy stepped the car up to eighty until we reached the outskirts of the capital, then as we neared some suburbs he slowed
down and we cruised at an innocent forty through them into
Washington, D.C., itself.

The orderliness of the streets, with their symmetrical patterns,
struck me at once. Jimmy drove round the tourist sights for my
benefit : the floodlit White House, the domed Capital and finally
the Folger Library. Its massive doors were shut and no light
showed in the building.

"Your tutor will be disappointed, Henry," said Jimmy.

"Oh well, perhaps I can come back sometime when it's open,"
I answered, though in fact I never did go there again.

Before we crossed the bridge over the River Potomac into
Arlington, Virginia, I noticed a large, oddly-shaped building only
half-constructed and asked Jimmy what it was going to be.

"It's going to be a new administrative centre," he told me.
"They call it The Pentagon."

We swung into the drive-in café about ten minutes later. It
was only about eight-thirty and not many people were in the
place. The café itself was pleasant enough, spotlessly clean, with
partitioned seating arrangements for four people at a table. We
sprawled on the foam rubber cushions and listened to a jukebox

number, *Five O'Clock Whistle,* while a waitress brought the
steaks. She had long legs enhanced by black nylon stockings; she
also had a soft, southern accent and a big smile for everybody.

"Southern charm," said Jimmy, winking.

We lazed and smoked after our steaks, that is to say, Jimmy and
I did. Daria didn't smoke and if she lazed she did it so that no one
noticed. Invisible relaxation.

I had a confused sense of the real and the unreal. Either the
war was unreal: the blackout at home, the bombing of cities,
the sinkings of ships, rationing, aerial dogfights. Or this roadhouse with its neutral atmosphere of peace and plenty was unreal.
I didn't know whether I'd slept and had a ghastly nightmare, or
if I was now living in a pleasant dream. A thin cold wind whined
outside the plate glass windows and I stared out into the darkness
which was unbroken by lights of any kind. We had come several
miles from the capital and the road was a lonely one, to-night at
least. This place must have been an oasis between Washington and
some other town. I didn't know which and didn't care. We might
have been on the moon for all I knew. Life seemed sad and
strange, but full of wonder. Here was I, lost for the time being,
in a foreign land, and sitting opposite me were two people who,
but for the Revolution and the migration of their parents, would
probably be *kulaks* in the Ukraine, in which case I should never
have met them, and even if I had we should not have been able
to converse. Brushing aside these idle speculations, now that I had
met them, and talked, and laughed with them, what next? Soon
I should return to my damp, dark island upon which German
bombs were falling—if we succeeded in getting back—and the
brother and sister sitting opposite me would be but two more
people I had met among hundreds in a cold, old war. Perhaps in
a few months, forgotten? I doubted it. I had grown fond of the
Donchenkos in the short time I'd known them.

In the fluorescent lighting Daria's face looked ethereal. Her
beauty was of the fragile sort, paradoxically, long lasting. Such
facial bone structure preserves beauty—but it was not for me. I
was just passing by. I tried to throw my mind off the Daria subject. When Jimmy went out to see about petrol for the car she said:

"You've been looking very thoughtful, Henry. Is anything the
matter?"

"No. Just one of those pleasant moods that are streaked with
sad thoughts, without anything really being the matter," I answered, thinking that Wordsworth had put it better.

Daria smiled.

"I see. Melancholy," she said.

"If you must name it, melancholy I suppose it is," I replied.

"Have you a girl in England?" Daria asked suddenly.

So suddenly that I laughed. If you look thoughtful women always think you are thinking of women.

"A girl? No. I'm just interested in nifty waitresses," I said.

Daria must have flushed pink, but in the café's moon-lighting she purpled faintly.

"I'm sorry. I was only joking," I said, but she was offended and we sat in silence until Jimmy came back a minute or two later.

"Did you get the juice?" I asked, standing up.

"Juice? Oh, you mean gas. Ha-ha! Did you hear that, Daria Henry calls gas 'juice'," he laughed.

I didn't think it very funny and Daria appeared not to have heard. We left the cool hygienic café and drove back to Baltimore On the way I told them of my previous night's visit to the club

"What sort of place was it?" Jimmy asked.

After I had described the night club he whistled through his teeth.

"Morelli's! You were lucky to get out of that place with even your one dollar. They might have slipped you a 'Mickey.' It's been done before there," cried Jimmy.

"A what?" I asked.

"A Mickey Finn. It's a knockout drink," explained Daria.

"Oh yes, I've heard of them on the films, but I thought the were only on the films," I said.

"For an educated man you still have a lot to learn," Daria commented, her humour returned.

"He's doing all right," Jimmy grinned over his shoulder, "give the man time."

Daria's teeth flashed in a dazzling smile.

"Sure. Plenty of time," she replied enigmatically.

VII

For the next three weeks I went everywhere with the Don chenkos, mostly with Jimmy and Daria, occasionally with one o the other, sometimes with the entire family to visit relations. W went to shows, plays, football matches, exhibitions of classica ballet at Daria's school, and to their friends' houses. On on occasion we went to a dinner party given by an elderly English woman who had lived in the United States for thirty years. Sh had gone completely native apart from retaining a preferenc for tea over coffee.

One of the guests, a fat, middle-aged man named Wallensteir

was apparently anti-British and kept trying to draw me into an argument. In the end he succeeded, but not until our hostess and the other ladies had left us alone with coffee and cigars for a few minutes.

"You Britishers," Wallenstein began aggressively, "you make fun of us Americans, but you come running to us as soon as you need help."

"Running?" I said. "Do I look breathless?"

I got a cheap laugh out of this feeble line from the others who disliked Wallenstein. He got angry.

"You can laugh," he snarled, "you can all laugh, but see if you think it's funny when the Army drafts you over into *their* war!"

He pointed a fat, manicured finger at me.

"I've no doubt they'll discover that even war has a funny side," I answered.

Wallenstein paid no attention to the remark.

"I remember how they dragged us into the last affair. . .!" he began to reminisce largely, but one of the men cut in:

"Were you in the Army or Navy?"

Wallenstein was completely taken aback.

"Well, neither, but——"

"But you said 'us'," another man pointed out.

"Shouldn't have said 'us'," Jimmy said, backing him up.

"Aw, hell, you know very well what I meant," grumbled Wallenstein. "You can't sidetrack me, no sir, why only last week I was nominated president of my club. I tell you that I can hold my own on points of debate without losing my temper. Now, where was I?"

"Just about to lose your temper," said another of the young men.

The others guffawed.

"I think you were about to tell us how you, or rather your compatriots, won the last war for England," I said.

"Yeah, and we'll win this one too," Wallenstein snapped.

"Jolly good. I always like to be on the winning side," I answered.

He sat back and grunted.

"You wouldn't be sitting here now, enjoying yourself, if it weren't for our boys," he said petulantly.

This remark infuriated me.

"What the devil do you mean by that?" I demanded.

He looked frightened at my sudden show of anger.

"Well, I mean, our Navy boys saw you safely across this side of the Pond didn't they? Unofficial escort, lease-lend, that sort of thing?"

He grinned feebly. It was true of course that the U.S. Navy were helping British shipping unofficially, but they hadn't helped the s.s. *Vesta* yet.

"If the United States Navy escorted us here they must have done so with submarines. We never saw a naval surface vessel, nor did we expect to. As a matter of fact, we came to Baltimore independent of any escort, yours or ours," I said.

There were loud cheers from the other men, but I cursed myself for having allowed Wallenstein to draw this information from me. Not that I thought it would be "useful to the enemy," but, as the consulate secretary had said, you couldn't be too careful.

"Rule, Britannia!" Daria sang, dancing into the room ahead of the other women, "Who won the argument?" she asked lightly.

"Henry did," said Jimmy.

Wallenstein looked cross again.

'Well," he said sullenly, "no enemy'll ever catch *this* country unawares."

"I hope you're right," I said.

Everybody else hoped he was right. Later as we drove down to the docks in Ronald's car, Daria said:

"I'm glad you got the better of that slob, Henry. He was leering at me all through dinner and made a pass at me as he helped me on with my coat."

"What was he doing there anyway? He didn't seem like a friend of Mrs. Hardcastle's," said Jimmy.

"He isn't," Daria answered. "He's a friend of a friend. Mrs. Hardcastle hadn't seen him until this evening. Nasty man!"

They dropped me at the dock entrance and I wandered along the quay to the *Vesta's* berth.

She wasn't there!

My heart stood still. They had had sudden orders to sail . . . I was left in a foreign country . . . technically a deserter from the Royal Navy . . . a traitor, almost. I ran wildly along the quay, looking for someone to confirm my worst fears. Oddly enough there was a light in the city morgue and two men were coming out of the doorway. I panted up to them.

"That ship that was tied up here, which way did she go?" I asked idiotically.

The two men looked at each other.

"There is only one way," one of them said.

"Out," said the other.

"Yeah," agreed the first.

"When did she shove off?" I asked breathlessly.

"This afternoon," said one man.

"About three," said the other, then they both asked:

"Why?"

I sat down wearily on the steps of the morgue.

"Because I should have been on her." I said.

I would give myself up to the police. No. I would go to the Donchenkos. No. That might get them into trouble, complicity or something or other. I would change my name, get a job ashore perhaps move inland. Or I would jump in the dock.

"Cheer up, son," said the first man. "She's probably just gone over to the grain wharf. She's a grain freighter, ain't she?"

I could have hugged the man.

"Of course she is!" I cried eagerly.

What a fool I was. As if the *Vesta* would have come all this way only to sail back again without a cargo. I asked the men to direct me to the grain wharf, which they did. It was about three miles distant by road, so I walked off with the two men, intending to get a taxi.

"Brrrr! I'm frozen," exclaimed one of the men as we hurried along. "Do you have to have them refrigerator things going all day in there?"

He meant in the morgue.

"Yeah," his friend said. "Gotta keep the meat fresh."

He turned to me.

"He's a new boy," he explained. "Just started to-day. Don't like the work. Ain't got no sense o' vocation."

He grinned and waved his hand. We had come to the road and I had hailed a cruising taxi.

The s.s. *Vesta* was at the grain wharf all right, tied up along-side a towering grain elevator and with huge pipes running down into her cargo hatches as if she were being stomach-fed. Grain dust lay thick as snow on the decks and I padded aboard, up the gangway, thankful not to wake the night watchman who was sleeping in the galley. All shore leave expired at midnight, offici-ally. It was now past one.

Next morning I learned from Colin that all the repairs had been completed and that we should be away in a day or two, once the grain had been loaded and trimmed. We were taking on maize, squaw corn—as the fourth engineer had called it. I stayed on board all that day, reading some books I had bought ashore, and writing letters to my parents and friends in England. There was a possibility that this was the last time they would hear from me, and this was not an unduly pessimistic view. The ship was old and her armament poor. We had been very lucky on the out-ward trip, but this was the easier run. Homeward bound, the wolf packs would be after us.

The next day we were told that leave would be cancelled as

from midnight. We were going out with the morning tide. I went ashore after lunch with the intention of having a final fling, spending the last of the dollars I had subbed a few days before. Also of course I wanted to see Jimmy and Daria for the last time. It was going to be awkward as we were under strict injunction not to reveal the time of the ship's departure to anyone. If anybody had been sufficiently interested they could have found out about it easily enough by simply strolling down to the docks and waving good-bye to us as we cast off. But such were the orders.

I telephoned the Donchenkos and they invited me to dinner at their house, but I declined, saying that to-night they should dine with me for a change. We met, Daria, Jimmy and I, at a little Greek restaurant which I had recently found gave good service, presented excellent food, and was not expensive. All the Greek places were pro-British as our troops were at the time fighting hard in Greece to keep the Nazis out.

"To-morrow's Saturday," exclaimed Jimmy suddenly, after we had finished our meal. "What about going to the ice rink? Can you skate, Henry?"

"A little," I said, frowning. "But I don't think I can manage it to-morrow night."

Daria looked up.

"Oh, do try to come," she said warmly. "You haven't seen me skate."

I had been told she was an expert and had looked forward to seeing her perform. I hesitated.

"Well, I'll see," I said, and changed the subject.

We went to see a film and then Jimmy and Daria said they would walk down to the docks with me. I told them that we were now at the grain wharf and that it was too far for them to come, but they insisted.

The ship loomed black and large, though she was in fact low in the water now that she had her cargo of maize. I had never seen her fully loaded before and she looked almost a submarine to me. Her hatches were battened down and the grain pipes were swung away from her decks. The *Vesta* looked ready for sea. Jimmy noticed it.

"Hey, you're all packed up! When are you shoving off?" he asked excitedly.

I didn't answer. Daria said quickly :

"You mustn't ask him such questions."

I was grateful to her.

"Oh, no. Sorry," muttered Jimmy.

After that we stood about for a few moments, not knowing what to say to one another. I turned to go aboard.

"Wait," said Daria.

I stopped and turned about. Jimmy had walked a little way along the quay, discreetly.

"Yes?" I said.

Daria was in my arms, her cheek soft and warm against mine. She was crying.

"It's no use," I said, "I'm just a visitor. Just a passer-by."

"You'll write? Perhaps you'll come back, some day."

I kissed her.

"I'll write," I said.

Jimmy returned and we shook hands.

"It's been great knowing you," he said quietly.

I turned and went up the gangway without looking back, though I was sure they were still standing on the quayside waiting for me to wave to them. But it was cold; they wouldn't stay long. I hurried down to my cabin and nearly bowled Colin over as I went through the mess.

"The mate's aboard," he said.

I pushed past him into my cabin and shut the door. When I woke up the next morning we were steaming slowly out of Chesapeake Bay, forever.

VIII

THE JOURNEY to Halifax, Nova Scotia, where we were to meet a homeward bound convoy, was cold and uneventful. The gun's crew exercised for an hour each day, despite their grumbles at first, for after nearly a month of inactivity they were stiff and slow. However, by the time Nantucket Island lay on our port quarter we had all regained most of our usual speed and agility, besides which, jumping about in the nipping air restored our spirits to something like normal. But as we neared Halifax our gun-drills were stopped by cold rain, sleet, snow and finally, ice.

We lay at anchor in the bay which had been frozen over with ice a foot thick, but this was now broken by shipping into thousands of fragments which bobbed and tossed on the waves. Icicles hung from our rigging and the deck was a mass of solid ice. The 4-inch gun, with its canvas cover frozen stiff and shining looked like some great grey mammoth of the Ice Age. The snow-covered landscape around the port looked cold and uninviting. There was no general shore leave for the crew, and nobody cared.

However, on the third day I managed to get ashore on gunnery business with the third mate, Mr. O'Neil. We had discovered that some of our Snowflakes had been damaged so I had to take them—half a dozen—to the stores to get them changed. The third mate had to attend a conference of ships' gunnery officers that afternoon, so we went ashore in the same boat, a water-taxi as they are called, which nosed its way gingerly between the miniature icebergs and finally tied up alongside a rickety wooden pier.

"That'll be two dollars," said the Canadian boatman.

The third paid him and as we stepped ashore he turned to me and said:

"Meet me here at six o'clock. We'd better get back to the ship before it's dark as these johnnies won't want to take their boats out then. Here's a couple of dollars for you. No, don't thank me. I got some money from the Old Man for expenses. Didn't know he'd got any Canadian cash aboard but it seems he keeps some. You can spend English currency in some places here, or change it at the banks—if you have any."

"Which I haven't," I said.

"No. I didn't think you would have," he grinned. "Well, so long."

With a wave of his hand he hurried off to his conference while I shouldered the box of rockets and set an unsteady course for DEMS stores. What the upshot of the gunnery officers' pow-wow was I never found out, for I received no fresh orders from either the third or the captain and concluded that there were none.

The stores were not far from the pierhead. I dumped the damaged rockets there, intending to pick up the replacements on the way back, but a surly chief petty officer acidly informed me that I had no business bringing DEMS supplies ashore myself, that they had a boat which went round to all the ships for that purpose and that the said boat would deliver the new rockets to us before the ship sailed. Thus freed of all responsibilities until six that evening, and with two dollars to spend. I set off for the town of Halifax at a brisk walk.

Halifax has not much to offer in the way of sights for tourists. On the side of Citadel Hill, which dominates the city, there is embedded a huge ship's anchor. It belonged to the *Mont Blanc*, an ammunition ship which caught fire and blew up in the harbour in 1917. The anchor was hurled two miles, whizzing like a meteorite, and there it was in the hillside. I didn't got to look at it. After all, I thought, it's only an anchor. This sentiment can be applied to almost anything one is too lazy to go and look at. Instead I wandered through a negro shanty town near the docks and listened to a coloured congregation singing hymns in a little wooden church which was nearly rocking with hallelujahs, while outside, on a patch of snow-cleared ground a bunch of young negroes squatted on their slender haunches shooting dice against the wooden wall. In composition and colour, though not style, the whole was a picture Ben Shahn might have painted.

I walked up Halifax's main street savouring the new smells. It was a delight to look in the well-stocked shop windows. I tried to browse in a bookshop but this was not looked upon with favour. Quick-sales assistants kept asking me if they could help. Perhaps they thought I couldn't read. I left the shop without buying anything, much to their undisguised chagrin, and went into a café.

A jukebox was beating out a crazy rhythm and two Canadian sailors were jiving and capering around the instrument. The only other customers were three men in civvies, obviously merchant seamen, obviously drunk. They surreptitiously tippled from a whisky bottle which they passed round underneath the table. Such a thing was illegal in Nova Scotia of course. No alcohol was supposed to be drunk on public premises or in steets or public transport. There were no pubs, bars or saloons but beer or whisky was obtainable from liquor stores if a permit was presented. Even then the ration was small : one bottle of whisky per month per man, or one dozen bottles of beer. I failed to see the point of all this. If it was supposed to prevent drunkenness it failed hopelessly for I saw more drunks in that one afternoon in Halifax than I saw in Baltimore in a month. Non-drinkers often gave or sold their permits to the boozers; liquor was brought ashore from ships and drunk in alleys, cinemas, lavatories, and I even saw a man underneath a seat in a tram swigging from a bottle. The illegality of public drinking added spice to its practice, I imagined. It is only fair to say, however, that the residents of the town were not the offenders (if "offenders" is the right word), the culprits being mainly seamen and perhaps soldiers stationed in the area. But then the residents or citizens had homes to drink their quota in— and anybody else's quota they could get hold of. Many of them used to save their stuff for two or three months, perhaps adding teetotallers' rations to their hoard, then a few friends would pool their collections and have a wild party which went on for days, until all the bottles were empty, when the hoarding would start again. It was in later visits to Halifax that I experienced these interminable parties after the months of squirrelling bottled beer and whisky. The Nova Scotians I met, being unused to regular drinking, soon got drunk and fought over women—and men— during their orgies.

I ordered a coffee and sat behind a newspaper listening to the obstreperous grumblings of the merchant seamen and waiting for trouble. At last one of them turned to the Canadians and shouted :

"Switch the bloody thing off !"

The sailors took no notice but continued to dance with clumsy steps around the machine.

"Turn the bastert off!" another of the merchant seamen roared in a thick, Clydeside accent.

At this the two Canadians looked up and the bigger of the two, a massive blur of a man, lumbered towards the table where the three men were sitting. He was chewing gum, hugely.

"What d'you Limeys say?" he growled.

The three Glaswegians looked stunned.

"Limeys!" gasped one of them. "He thinks we're English!"

They rose as one man and waded into the big Canadian, his pal, and the café proprietor. The latter had come up in rear of the second sailor, in case of trouble. In case! Fists and feet flew in Gorbals fashion from the merchant seamen. The café proprietor was flung back against his jukebox which rocked violently and stopped playing abruptly.

"That's shut the bastert up!" shouted one of the seamen joyously.

He then turned to the more earnest business of filling in the already ugly face of the big sailor. At one blow of a Glasgow fist the giant staggered back against the counter sending bottles and glasses flying and crashing in all directions. A crowd had begun to gather outside the door, attracted by the noise. They stood on the pavement peering eagerly in. I drank my coffee stood up and went out into the street, after leaving a small tip beside my cup. Entertainment tax.

I wandered back down the main street calling in one or two shops for odds and ends to take back to the ship. There were still a couple of hours to beguile and as there was nothing else to do I went to a cinema and sat in the cheapest seats, next to a man who periodically took quick swigs at a flask without removing his eyes from the screen for an instant. Some Haligonians—if this is the noun substantive for inhabitants of Halifax—took whisky to the pictures as we take sweets, peanuts or cigarettes. The film was *The Thief of Baghdad* and it made a pleasing escape, but when I came out it was not yet dark and the world seemed colder starker and more harsh than before I went in. I set off for the jetty where I was to meet the third mate feeling thoroughly depressed. People were hurrying to their homes in the suburbs by tram or car and some of the shops were already shut. I envied the people as I saw them climbing into their big substantial cars. They were going home to warmth and security, good food, the radio, perhaps wife and children, perhaps hoarded liquor. But it was only a passing envy. I was impatient to get back to England to find out if we were going back to Baltimore next trip. There was a remote possibility that we might, but only a remote one. The s.s. *Vesta* was a tramp; she seldom went to the same place twice in two trips. It might be South America next time, or anywhere. Next time. At the pier I shivered, waited for the third and counted the grim outlines of the ships waiting, like the *Vesta*, for the convoy to form. They seemed black and inhuman, these twenty-nine or was it thirty ships tugging at their anchors, but I knew that each of them had an identity, a village ship-life of its own, or perhaps one could say that each ship was a paradigm of the universe in little, a microcosm with its hierarchy of officers, its citizen-sailors . . . I was becoming lost in comparisions.

"Quiet run ashore?" a cheerful voice asked.

Mr. O'Neil stood beside me.

"Yes, thank you," I said. "They are going to send the rockets out to the ship before we sail."

"Better look sharpish then," he commented.

When we got back on board the Snowflakes had already been delivered. DEMS stores had wasted no time; there was none to waste. We sailed at dawn on the following day.

IX

A CONVOY SETTING out is an impressive sight and as this was my first experience of being in one I was fascinated by the procedure of getting into positions, or stations, as they are called, and by the variety of craft that made up the armada : several tankers, general cargo ships of all shapes and sizes, a cargo-passenger ship, while darting about round the outskirts of the convoy, urging the merchantmen into their correct places with farm dog determination, were two destroyers and three corvettes.

Our station number was 1.2, which meant that we were the second ship of the port flank, an exposed position. The crew did not like it.

"Just the place to cop a bloody packet first," the cook grumbled in the galley, while the bos'n went about telling everybody he had told them so.

It was comforting, however, to see the long slender form of a destroyer racing to and fro upon our port side and to know that she had ears for submarines and plenty of depth-charges to hurl and drop over the side. As the destroyer swept close by us from time to time the sailors on her decks would shout and wave to us while we would bawl back at them. Often I wanted to shout :

"I'm one of *you*! I'm in the Navy. I don't belong on this rotten old tub. It's nothing to do with me!"

When "our" destroyer sheered off to another part of the convoy we felt that our ship was old and vulnerable. I wished I hadn't volunteered to leave general service for the DEMS. I was sure I wouldn't have done if only I'd been drafted to a ship on reaching barracks instead of kept hanging about for a month, scrubbing out petty officers' lavatories and fighting for food in Jago's (the vast dining-hall in Devonport Barracks). Perhaps now, I thought, I should be dashing about at twenty-five knots up and down the flank of some convoy, instead of crawling along at eight knots in this one.

For seven dreary days we zigzagged on a north easterly course. The crew were morose and moody, partly because of the weather which was monotonously cold and grey. There is a kind of elation or exhilaration in rough weather. A storm is something to defy and gives you a sense of victory when it is over—provided it hasn't sunk you—but a dull grey sky and a heaving, grey-green sea never stimulated anybody.

I began to feel lonely and depressed. America seemed to belong to the distant past, England to the distant future, the *Vesta* to no particular time or place. We had not yet come to the U-boat fringe, the main attack area, 20° west. On March 6th we had heard over the W.T. that the Prime Minister had announced:

"In view of various German statements we must assume that the BATTLE OF THE ATLANTIC has begun."

Cheering news when we were just approaching mid-Atlantic. We knew that the heavy cruiser *Hipper*, together with the battle-cruisers *Scharnhorst* and *Gneisenau* were raiding in the North Atlantic, that there were at least a dozen U-boats knocking about somewhere, probably only a few hundred miles away, waiting for us, and that Admiral Doenitz ("Doughnuts") had begun his March offensive with particularly brutal wolf-pack tactics. Convoys were being attacked by half a dozen subs. at a time and many of our ships were finding the bottom of the Western Ocean. Who passed on all this heart-warming information I do not know, but it was picked up by the galley wireless and was quite accurate, as I later found out. We were in a part of the Atlantic known as The Gap because it was unpatrolled by aircraft either from Canada or Britain, being outside their fuel-range. A little later in the war the Germans called it The Black Pit as they had sunk so many of our ships there. But later still, in 1943, air cover was provided by small, light aircraft carriers which sailed with convoys and whose aircraft bridged the gap.

"It's too bloody quiet," the Fiver said to me one day.

We had reached 60° north and nearly 20° west.

"It's also too bloody cold," I answered, stamping my feet on the gun platform and flailing my arms against my body.

I was so padded with sweaters and lifejacket under my duffel coat that my arms stuck out like penguins' flippers.

"We're altering course at noon. Turning south. Be all right in a day or two—as far as temperature is concerned," the Fiver said, adding the last phrase with a grimace.

I hadn't seen much of him since we'd been at sea. He seemed to prefer to keep himself to himself, reading in his cabin when off duty, as indeed most of us did who weren't inclined to play cribbage either in the galley or the engineers' mess. But sometimes I would meet him in the galley where we would sit and listen to the gossip by the warm, friendly stove, with our legs braced and feet on the coal bunker against the sickening roll of the *Vesta*. Then the bos'n would appear, swearing and grumbling, prophesying doom for all, and we would go out on deck to pace up and down in the cutting wind.

As we turned south-east the weather did improve. I began to shed a sweater a day as it grew warmer until I was down to one blue jersey, my lifejacket and duffel coat and found that I could lower my arms to my sides and get things out of pockets which had been inaccessible a few days before owing to the bulk of clothing I had worn.

In the sea area known as Rockall the sun began to shine and cheered everyone on board. We were well in the U-boat region now, about 15° west, and we hadn't seen a thing. Perhaps we had given them the slip by steaming so far north? May be the packs had been sent to concentrate on some other area, Biscay for instance? Speculations multiplied, hopes ran high, the galley wireless spluttered and crackled with good news. We were going to unload at Liverpool and the ship might be in for a few weeks as the repair job done to the bridge in the States was only temporary, a patching till the ship got back to the U.K. Some of the crew got the Channels. This interesting term sounds like a variation of D.T.'s but simply means that the sufferers behaved as if the ship were already in the North, the St. George's or the English Channels and began to prepare to go ashore, washing and ironing their shore-going clothes, sorting out the things they intended to declare to the customs men from those they hoped to smuggle off the ship after the officials had gone ashore. All this was extremely optimistic considering the fact that we were still at least five hundred miles off the coast of Northern Ireland, by no means out of the wood, as they say, yet.

One afternoon I caught Colin in his pantry engaged in duty

and excise evasion tactics. He had stripped away some of the woodwork near the edge of one bulkhead and was busy forcing flat plugs of tobacco sideways into the slots he had had made. He started guiltily when he saw me watching this operation.

"Ye'll no tell anyone, will ye?" he breathed.

I promised not to.

"But won't they see the tobacco?" I asked, worried by the way the brown edges of the plugs stood out against the white paint-work of the bulkhead.

"Not when ah've painted it the same colour as the bulkhead, man," he said, surprised that I hadn't worked out a simple thing like that for myself.

So was I.

For several days now the whole convoy had carried out emergency turns, the point of which I didn't understand at first. At one blast of the commodore's ship's siren the convoy would swing round 45° to port, then at a second blast another 45° so that we were then sailing at right angles. If two consecutive blasts were sounded the convoy would swing to starboard instead. At night red flares would be fired from a Very pistol if a port swing was to be indicated, green ones if a starboard turn was required. We did not practise the turns at night as light signals were to be used during an actual attack only, but we knew what the drill was.

Gun-drills which we had nearly every day were beginning to seem pointless to the gun's crew. They grumbled and moaned about wanting overtime each afternoon they turned out, until one day I lost my temper and shouted at them:

"What about my overtime then? Your company pays me the great sum of sixpence a day. The Navy gives me three-and-six. Add that up and see if it comes to more than a fifth of your money! These gun-drills might help to save *your* skins as well as the rest of the crew's you know."

I was silent after that and so were they, until Baines said:

"We ain't got nothing against you, Guns."

He kicked, self-consciously, at the gun mounting with his sea-boot.

"Naw, we don't mean nothing personal," Johnston added, also looking slightly flustered and guilty.

I remained silent and aloof. Pimply Harris offered me a cigarette and I accepted it with dignity. But it served as an ice-breaker. We were united again and I felt that a moral victory had been gained. I realized, too, the power of the sulk. There were no more grumbles about drills, but then, there were no more drills.

The next night I was sleeping peacefully in my bunk when at about 11.30 the action stations bell began to ring furiously in the mess. I was dressed apart from seaboots, lifejacket and duffel, so I jumped out of my bunk and put these on then rushed up on deck into what at first seemed to be Hell itself. The sky was lit with a bright orange glow which seemed to emanate from somewhere on our starboard side. I hurried aft and climbed onto the gun-platform, bawling orders to clear the gun for action at members of the gun's crew who were clambering up after me. Then suddenly I stopped and stood as if my boots were frozen to the deck! There before my eyes was surely one of the most horrible and terrifying sights of the war: a tanker blazing from stem to stern with men visibly roasting alive on her decks. We could hear the roar of the flames and feel the heat of the blazing petrol on our faces as the ship, not more than two hundred yards away, still appeared to be going slowly ahead, though this may have been an illusion caused by the dynamic beauty of the leaping flames. Some of the crew managed to jump overboard, their clothes alight, but the sea itself was an inferno of sheeted fire all round the ship. There was no escape for any of the sixty men who formed the tanker's crew.

It could have been only a few minutes, but it seemed centuries that I stood watching that fantastic sight, the first real horror of the war at sea that I had witnessed. With a conscious effort I dragged my eyes from the scene and looked at the other gunners. Each man seemed drawn into himself, standing each in his aura of personal fear with eyes a thousand years old. It was as if we had gazed upon the eternal fire of traditional Hell for one brief instant.

I heard my own voice with a ventriloquial remoteness—it was almost like a recording—telling the men to load the gun. It had suddenly occurred to me that apart from the tanker we were alone, a splendid target for a U-boat, silhouetted as we were against the glow from the other ship. The convoy must have scattered as soon as the attack was made and would no doubt reform at some pre-arranged rendezvous, but meanwhile we were alone, or so I thought. I wondered why we hadn't heard any depth charges from the escorts. Perhaps the submarine or submarines were on the surface and the destroyers weren't getting any Asdic contacts. This suspicion was confirmed when the third mate's voice rasped out:

"Submarine on surface, port quarter!"

He had been sweeping the darkness on the port side with a pair of powerful night-glasses.

"Range?" I queried, shoving the gun round with my hips.

"Six hundred yards approximately," came the reply.

"Range six hundred," I repeated mechanically, setting the sight.

I squinted down the telescope but could see nothing at first then I thought I saw a dim shape blacker than the sea. I licked my lips. They were dry and cracked.

"Stand by," I said.

"You won't hit him in this light but you might scare him off," said the third.

I doubted it, but we might as well try.

"Open fire!" the third yelled.

We fired rapidly in the general direction of the U-boat with about a dozen rounds of H.E., but I could see nothing through the telescope except darkness and smoke from the torpedoed tanker.

"Cease firing!" shouted the third. "There's a destroyer coming up. He's going to ram!"

We stopped firing and the gun crew gave a cheer.

"Good old Navy!" Baines bellowed.

I looked down the telescope again but the cap might have been on the end of it for all I could see.

"What's happening?" I shouted up to the third who was in the 12-pounder turret.

"Can't see. Range increasing too fast," he answered.

The old *Vesta* had turned her tail and we were thumping along flat out at thirteen knots, just as we had done when we spotted the sub. on the way out. It was just past mid-night. We remained closed up at the gun until it was full daylight and we had joined up with the rest of the convoy. The tanker which had been hit was the one which had been ahead of us and we were ordered to move up into her position, 1.1, so that we were now the first ship the port flank of the convoy. It was like stepping into a dead man's shoes. Just after eight o'clock the destroyer sidled up and hailed us:

"*Vesta* ahoy! Your gunfire helped to direct us to surfaced U-boat last night. She was successfully rammed and sank with all hands. Thank you very much."

The loud hailer clicked off and the destroyer swung away to port. Some matelots standing near the depth-charges astern waved and cheered. We waved back, too tired to cheer. We had all seen the kink in the ship's stem piece and guessed that she had made a kill before they told us. The phone rang and I answered it.

"Congratulations, gunners! You can stand down now. Gun layer. Get yourself some breakfast. Ye deserve it!" said the voice of the first mate, then he rang off before I could reply.

We stowed the ammo, sponged out the gun and slipped the breech cover on, then the watch broke up and I went below to get some breakfast and a few hours' sleep. It seemed the odds were even : one of ours sunk with no survivors, one of theirs sunk with no survivors. About a hundred men dead on both sides in one night in one small area of the Atlantic. So this was the war at sea, I thought as I cut into a sausage. I was about to eat it when suddenly I saw the burning tanker with the men running along her decks, their clothing alight. I fancied I smelt burning flesh and overcome with nausea I fled the mess and rushed on deck where I was violently sick for about half an hour, mostly with spasms of dry heaves. Exhausted and feeling ghastly, I staggered down to my cabin and lay on the bunk trying to think of anything but the tanker and her roasting crew. My clothes smelt of cordite and petrol fumes, and I fancied burnt flesh also. I got up and stripped, washed myself well then changed into some clean jean trousers and a different jersey. I lay down again, feeling better, and went to sleep almost at once.

X

I AWOKE WITH a thundering headache at about three in the afternoon. Colin gave me some tea and aspirin and a slice of toast. I ate the toast carefully then rolled a cigarette and lay back smoking and trying to remember who and what I was and why I was where I was. Nothing made sense. I got up, put on sea-boots, lifejacket and oilskin, then went on deck. The sky was dark with rain clouds but the weather seemed warmer. Our destroyer was ploughing heavily through an oily swell, throwing up an enormous bow wave as high as the artificial one painted on her hull. The destroyers were always camouflaged thus to make it difficult for enemy sightsetters to estimate their targets' speeds.

The old *Vesta* was rolling painfully. She would occasionally pitch and plunge so that her stern lifted out of the water with the screw whirring and the whole aft part of the ship whickering like a springboard. It was small wonder really that she hadn't already broken her back as the bos'n constantly predicted she would. I stood on the juddering gun-platform watching the rest of the convoy. They were keeping stations well and I waved to a gunner on a tanker in the next column to ours, but he must have been looking in the opposite direction for he didn't wave back, or perhaps he was feeling too apprehensive to notice. He was on a benzine tanker.

To keep my mind off the previous night's horror I busied myself cleaning the 4-inch. I cleaned and oiled the breech mechanism and coated it lightly with grease, then I put the cover back on and, after checking the ready-use ammunition lockers, went below for a spell before starting my long dusk watch. Upon my return to the guns at about five-thirty I looked around the convoy and noticed that on the tanker next to ours there were several members of the crew—those not on watch presumably—huddled round the stern of the vessel, wearing lifejackets but not heavy coats or seaboots. Their intention was obvious : if their ship was torpedoed they would jump straight over the side, hoping to beat the flames by a few seconds. This has been done and the few tankermen who were powerful enough swimmers have either outstripped the burning fuel as it raced towards them, or cast off their lifejackets and swum underwater to the edge of the flames and then been picked up by escort or rescue ships. But most sailors are not swimmers of this championship class, so the chances of such a survival were very small.

The Fiver came aft and leant against the rail, smoking and looking towards the benzine tanker.

"Rather them than us," he commented. "Poor bastards. At least we've only got a cargo of chicken-feed."

"Not forgetting the oil in our bunkers and the fact that our magazine is now on the water-line?" I reminded him.

It was true. Now that the ship was loaded the mag. had sunk to a dangerous line for torpedo attacks.

"Christ. I hadn't thought of that. Why the hell did you tell me? Now I shan't be able to sleep to-night," the Fiver groused.

"Who will, if it's anything like last night?"

"Och away! The Navy's settled that bastard's hash. It was probably the only submarine within miles of the area."

"But we're not in that area now. Been travelling since then."

"You're a bloody pessimist," shouted the Fiver. "Anyway, I'm going to get some gear ready to step ashore in dear old Glasgy Toon."

He shuffled off in the gathering gloom and I brought my binoculars to bear on the dark horizon.

By my reckoning we were now just about in the middle of the recognized graveyard of Allied shipping during this phase of the war, 55° north, 12° west, roughly, still a few hundred miles off the coast of Northern Ireland. I picked up the telephone and twiddled the handle.

"Bridge," said a homuncular voice.

It was the one I wanted, the third mate's.

"Mr. O'Neil? Shall I close up the gun's crew, sir?"

"What for?"

"Well, in case of trouble."

The gunnery officer's question seemed stupid to me.

"No. Not unless the Captain says so. You won't be able to see anything soon—unless we get a firework display. We'll get them up there at the double if anything happens. All right?"

I supposed it was all right. Anyway, it wasn't my ship. I hung up the receiver and resumed peering through the glasses, lowering them now and then to rest my eyes, in the manner taught. Every catspaw seemed to have been made by a periscope. I thought of wicked Aryan eyes watching us, waiting for an opportunity to give the order: *"Rohr Eins! Achtung!—Ll-o-o-ss!"* and the silver fish bounding towards us at forty miles an hour. I thought of the U-boat crew at their stations, quiet, tense, haggard but still hard, blond, unsmiling, propaganda-fed and British-hating. I too, of course, was a victim of propaganda to think thus of U-mariners, but the curious thing to me was that I had no more hatred of the German sailors than a white pawn has for a black. We were all pieces in a game played by our governments, a monstrous, bitter, brutal, stupid game. I believe that with the exception of the very gullible and some of those who had suffered personal loss, my attitude was fairly typical of men of my generation engaged in the war—and perhaps of many older men too. Let dictators rant and prime ministers make their sonorous, Ciceronian speeches; I and many like me would remain cynically aloof. Let them stuff their rhetoric and try living in overcrowded barracks, or on benzine tankers, or in submarines, themselves.

I stayed in the 12-pounder turret until just after nine o'clock, then went into the galley for cocoa and sandwiches. The Fiver was in there, the bos'n, the saloon steward, cook and Colin the mess-boy. The cook and the steward were playing cribbage.

"Sandwich for you over there, Guns," said the cook without looking up. "Cocoa in the can."

I thanked him and poured myself a mug of thick, steaming cocoa, then took the bully sandwich and wolfed it. I hadn't realized how hungry I was until I tasted the food. The bos'n gave me a big, prehistoric grin.

"Been off your food, boy?" he asked.

My cheeks bulged, so I just nodded. I unslung my binoculars (these, incidentally, had been sent out to the ship by DEMS Halifax after a special request had been made for them) and stuffed them into my duffel coat pocket, then I tried to sip the scalding mud but burnt my lips, so I set it down on the coal bunker to cool. It was hot in the galley with the stove door open and the coals glowing a brilliant yellowish red. By the time I had drunk my cocoa and the bos'n had shambled off to the fo'c'sle I was beginning to sweat in my thick clothing, so I stepped out on deck. I stood for a moment or two, shutting and opening my eyes to accustom them to the darkness before going up to the guns. The galley door was open on this, the lee side of the ship and I heard the flap of the greasy, double canvas blackout curtains in the doorway as somebody else stepped out on deck. It was the Fiver, yawning.

"Think I'll turn in," he was just saying, when a green flare fired from the commodore startled the darkness over our heads, then cometed into the sea.

"Forty five degrees to starboard," I said. "There must be something about over there."

I pointed vaguely over the port side as we heard the telemotor whirring like a giant grasshopper when the wheel was swung over and the ship heeled slightly on to her new course. Another flare greened the night sky.

"Another forty five," said the Fiver.

Again the telemotor whirred and the *Vesta* swung round the full ninety degrees. We were now steaming at right angles to our former course. The escorts must have made a contact with their Asdics and I decided to muster the gun's crew, irrespective of the third mate's orders. I started to tell the Fiver of my intention :

"I'm going to——"

I got no further. The ship suddenly staggered from an impact as if she'd been hit by an express train. I felt as if a blanket had been thrown over my head before I was lifted off the deck and hurled towards the stern. I felt, rather than heard, the explosion as the torpedo burst, it seemed, within the ship's oil bunkers. Then there was nothing but blackness.

It could have been only a few minutes later that I sat up in what seemed to be a red mist. I could hear shouting and screaming from somewhere behind me. Standing up, I discovered where I was : right on the overhang of the stern, saved from going overboard by two thin wire rails ! I was saturated with fuel oil and sea water, the deck was covered with the stuff and the ship was listing heavily to port, the side where we'd been hit. I took my coat off and flung it over the rails. Now I could move better. Flames, mast-high, shot out of the bunkers and I stared, fascinated, for a few moments until I remembered that the magazine was near the bunkers and must soon be affected by the heat from the blazing oil. I slithered across the metal deck to a sprinkler valve used for flooding the mag. and tried to turn it. It stuck fast. Cursing I remembered that it was always kept padlocked so that it couldn't be turned on accidentally, that I kept the key, and that I had just thrown it, in the pocket of my duffel coat, into the drink ! I could see figures hurrying about on the after-boat-deck just above the gun platform, the ship's siren was sounding

six blasts for ABANDON SHIP, so I scrambled onto the platform to
make my way to my boat station.

"Help!" a voice cried in the redness. "Help! Gunner! Henry!
Don't leave me! Help!"

Bewildered, I looked round, wondering who was calling me and
where from. The voice was familiar, but it was like hearing your
name called in a dream. The cry came again:

"Help! Gunner! Help!"

It seemed to come from somewhere under the boat-deck, near
the galley. The Fiver! He had been with me when it happened. I
clambered back down the slippery rungs of the gun-platform
ladder and slithered stumblingly along the deck to the galley door.
It was light enough to see the Fiver lying on deck a few yards
from the galley, his leg caught under the deck piping. He saw me
and stopped shouting but set up a great howl of pain and fear:

"Oh, Gunner! Mah leg! Mah bloody leg's broken!"

I worked his leg free of the piping and began to drag him
along the sloping, slippery deck towards the guns, he howling
and screaming with pain all the time. I supposed that his leg must
really be broken. It was. On the boat-deck there were still people
trying to clear the boat in a lubberly fashion—fortunately for us,
or we should have been left on the ship—and I shouted up for
someone to help me to get the Fiver up there. The saloon steward
heard me and came down readily enough. Together we got the
Fiver on to the boat-deck and with an effort into the boat, which
though it was slung outboard on its davits was in fact touching
the ship's side, owing to the heavy list to port. This position would
have made it difficult for skilled sailormen to get the boat away
in a hurry, and there were no A.B.s or deck officers here to help.
The wooden boat-deck was ablaze in patches where fuel oil had
spattered it. Colin was lying flat on his back in some sort of gibbering fit near one of these fire pools, his eyes rolling wildly in a
mask of black oil which covered his face, his lips moving as if
in frantic prayer, while his heels beat a tattoo on the deck. He
looked like Al Jolson singing "Mammy" horizontally, but this
was not the time to tell him so. The second steward and I picked
him up and slung him into the boat after the Fiver. He was light,
like a child. Then, with several turns round the staghorns, we
lowered the boat, gingerly, into the water, its strake rubbing
down the ship's side all the way. I was thankful for the boat drills
I had had at H.M.S. Ganges, on first joining the Navy, for it
seemed that only the second steward and myself, of those trapped
on the aft part of the ship, had any idea how to lower a boat.
When I got to the scene of panic the cook and his mate were trying to lower away without first slipping the gripes.

Once the boat was in the water the steward and I leapt for the falls and slid down them with burning palms we didn't feel until afterwards. Neatly, we both dropped into the boat. Somebody was trying to free the painter which still secured us to the ship like some wretched umbilical cord.

"Knife!" he shouted.

By some accident I had my pusser's dirk in my trouser pocket. I opened the blade and handed the knife to the cook, who, now I could see, was the man asking for it. He snatched it out of my hand and began sawing the rope, cursing loudly until at last we were free.

"Hurray! Any more for the Skylark?" somebody bawled.

"Get the oars out quick!" I shouted. "The magazine's likely to go up any minute."

"Christ, I hadn't thought of that," said the cook.

Nobody else had either, it seemed, until then. I was suddenly knocked off my feet as somebody swung an oar round in my direction. I picked myself up out of the bottom of the boat, grabbed at the oar, stuck it in a rowlock and pulled. Fortunately there was not a very heavy sea running and we managed in a few minutes to put a couple of hundred yards between ourselves and the blazing *Vesta*.

"Rest," I said to the others.

We flopped over our oars like rag dolls and, breathing harder than I'd ever breathed for my college on the Isis, or during boat-pulling practice in the Stour estuary off Harwich, I watched the *Vesta* belching forth her smoke and flames like the Roman fire goddess whose name she bore. There was a deafening roar as the magazine stores were touched off, a thousand flying flaming fragments soared into the air and we all ducked down in the bottom of the boat. We could hear them fall hissing into the sea around us, miraculously missing our craft. When we looked up the *Vesta* was gone.

That was the end of my first ship.

There was no point in wasting our energy as we had nowhere in particular to row to, so we just kept the boat's head into the wind and hoped for an early rescue. The Fiver, who had fallen into a merciful faint when first put into the boat, had come round now and lay sobbing with agony in the stern sheets where some-one had lifted him. The cook was talking gently to him. Colin was crouched up in the bows, calmer now. I looked round to see who the others were. Carsen, the second engineer, the second steward and the assistant cook had oars as well as myself.

"Wonder what happened to the others?" I said to the second

steward (he and the saloon steward were the same person, by the way) who was my opposite rowing number.

"Got away in the 'midship's boats, I expect," he answered. "I saw both boats get away before us."

"What about the engine-room people, those who were on watch?" I asked.

"We're all right," said a strong Welsh voice.

I turned round and saw the third engineer, together with a fireman and donkeyman lounging back against the gunwhales.

"It vos a good yob you had the presence of mind to stop the engines, Third, or ve should never had got the boats avay vithout swamping them," commented the Dane.

"Bridge rang 'Stop Engines', so I did, that's all," said the third modestly.

"Did anybody hear 'Abandon Ship' sounded off?" someone asked.

"Yes," I said, "I heard it over the noise of the fire. Six blasts."

"Good oh then. We didn't leave the ship without permission," said the donkeyman.

A few of us laughed. We were still near the rest of the convoy for we could see occasional black shapes every time we lifted on a wave-crest. I prayed that nothing would run us down. Suddenly there was a dull explosion and another tanker burst into flames, possibly it was the benzine one which had been next to us. Snowflake rockets went up in the distance, presumably from the commodore's vessel, as they were supposed to be the first to fire them. At this given signal other ships sent up their Snowflakes and the effect was one of brilliant moonlight as the rockets burst like huge flowers, cascading their hundreds of shimmering bright petals over the dark waters. We could see many of the ships now, heading away from us in all directions, they seemed.

"Now watch the fun and games," muttered the third engineer.

Almost as soon as he said this we heard a series of explosions and saw no less than five ships torpedoed, two more of them tankers. It was almost as if the snowflakes had been just what the Germans were waiting for to help them to pick their targets, for this was obviously a periscope-depth attack and there was nothing to see on the surface except our own ships. Moreover it seemed like the work of more than one submarine. Probably one had been used to lure the port side destroyer away and make the convoy alter course while dead ahead the pack waited and picked us off when we had presented our beams as convenient targets to them. At least this was the tactic as it appeared to us. We sat for an hour or so in lonely darkness after the last Snowflake had melted. We could see the flickering fires of the burning ships in the distance and hear the muffled deep sea thunder of depth charges, then there was nothing but darkness, and silence, and cold. We were all soaked to the skin with fuel oil and sea. Now the boat was shipping water over the gunwales as the wind got up, and we had difficulty in keeping head on. We fished the sea-anchor out of the locker and streamed the funnel of canvas over the stern. This made a considerable difference, but the water was up to our knees before the bailers were found and those not using oars began scooping the sea out from between the thwarts. Those, that is, except the Fiver and Colin.

The dark shape of some vessel loomed up, not very high out of the water.

"I'll give 'em a flash with the torch," said the third.

"It might be a sub.," I warned him.

He took no notice, possibly thinking that we should drown anyway as we were now shipping far more water than could be bailed out, and began to flash an SOS. We sat tense, waiting for a burst of machine-gun fire if it should be a submarine we were signalling to. A beautiful English loud-hailer voice floated to us over the waves and out of the darkness :

"Please put that light out. We can see you clearly and will pick you up. Stand by as we come alongside."

My companions in the boat raised a cheer.

"It could still be a U-boat," I pointed out.

I had heard that many of the German commanders spoke more than Oxford English. They sometimes took prisoners, officers and naval gunners if there were any. The rest they filled with lead—perhaps. I didn't relish either the idea of being shot up or taken prisoner and being depth-charged by my own side. Suddenly as the black shape grew bigger I heard an unmistakable Liverpool accent :

"Easy up ther, Whacker. That's it now, la."

Some anonymous matelot was talking to his chum on deck. They were probably fixing a scramble-net in position for us. I felt a sudden rush of joy and gratitude at this homely voice which proclaimed, in these circumstances, the nationality of the ship far more than officer's clipped, universal, "Oxford" speech. As the ship came closer we shipped our oars and waited for a heaving line to be thrown. Something whizzed over our heads and splashed into the sea, the monkey's fist on the end of the line. Half a dozen pairs of hands clutched at the thin rope. The cook's caught it.

"Make it fast to your painter," said a voice from the deck.

"Haven't got one," answered the cook. "You'll have to heave us in on this."

He held fast to his end of the line and gradually we were hauled alongside the naval vessel which I could now see was a corvette, one of the escorts which had looked after the tail of the convoy and was now acting as rescue ship. The ship's deck seemed to be crowded with figures. Hands reaching down plucked somebody out of our boat each time she rose on the crest of a wave. We were alongside the after-deck which had only about six feet of free-board. I stayed in the boat to help to get the Fiver out. It was difficult as we had to lift him horizontally, then wait for the boat to heave itself upwards before we could thrust the Fiver up to the sailors on deck. We managed it after three attempts but as soon as we had let go of him the boat sank with a sideways lurch into a trough, I lost my balance and fell backwards into the sea. I had no drowning man's last look at his life flashed on his mental screen and lasting five seconds, which we are told all drowning men are privileged to enjoy, perhaps because I wasn't due to drown yet. My kapok jacket kept me up and somebody came down the scramble-net and helped me to get a hand and foot-hold. The same man led me dripping and stumbling along the deck to the fo'c'sle.

I had never been on a corvette before and was surprised to see how small the crew's accommodation was. Perhaps it seemed smaller because it was packed with other survivors, including the rest of the *Vesta's* crew who had apparently been picked up al-most immediately. Most of them weren't even wet and I felt annoyed about this. They too should have been soaked in filthy oil and sea water, but some of them looked just as I'd seen them on the *Vesta*. They leaned on mess-tables or lay on the deck smoking, almost insolently, it seemed to me. The Fiver had been laid on a table and a sick-berth attendant was putting his leg in splints. The Fiver grinned through his tears at me as I passed. He held out his hand and grabbed my arm tightly.

"Thanks, Henry," he said. "Sorry I made such a fuss."

"I should have made a much bigger one," I assured him.

A matelot stuck a cigarette in his mouth and lit it for him. He let go of my arm and tried to pull shakily at the fag. I went across to talk to the third mate.

"Hello, Guns, you look a bit wet," he said affably.

"You seem to have done all right," I answered ruefully.

He was no longer an officer of mine now. My articles with the *Vesta's* company had ceased the moment "Abandon Ship" had sounded off.

"Aw, cheer up. It might have been worse," grinned O'Neil, "The old Fiver's our only casualty. Look at those poor devils."

He nodded towards the other side of the mess-deck where a group of lascar seamen were huddled together. All were swathed in bandages and sat with their heads bowed in fatalistic attitudes.

"Only survivors of a ship carrying iron ore. They were blown into the drink. It's a miracle they were picked up, but they'll probably all be dead before morning. Ship sank in two minutes," the third mate said.

I looked at the thin, shivering bodies of the lascars, their heads bowed between their bony knees. But I was too wet and cold to feel much compassion.

"What's the time now?" I asked the third, my mind too stunned to say anything but unimportant things.

O'Neil looked at his watch.

"Quarter to two."

Was that all? I seemed to have been messing about in boats all night. A group of big men all dirty with oil like myself were talking together by the next table.

"Who are they?" I asked the third.

"Norwegians. Their tanker caught a packet. Luckily they were only carrying crude oil. It burns slowly—well, fairly slowly—compared with spirit. Half of them managed to get away."

A few of the corvette's crew were suspended in hammocks, the watch below. One stoker snored noisily. It seemed incredible that anyone could sleep with all this excitement going on, but I supposed that they were used to it and had become accustomed to snatching an hour or two's sleep whenever possible. Another man leaned out of his hammock and said :

"You a matelot, Jan?"

I was wearing pusser's trousers and he must have noticed the large flap in place of the civilian flies.

"Yes," I answered. "I'm a Guz rating—in the DEMS racket now."

Guz was the sailors' name for Devonport depôt. I gathered that this man was one too by his addressing me as "Jan"—the west country equivalent of Jack or Mac which you use if you don't know the other fellow's name. The other two naval depôts were Chats—Chatham and Pompy—Portsmouth. Guz or Guzz, I think, is so called from guzzle, a west country seaman's word for drizzle. It is very appropriate if you know the climate of the south west.

"Have a tickler," said the man in the hammock.

He handed me his tin and I rolled a fat oily fag. He then leaned over and said apologetically :

"There ain't no spare gear left for you to change into, but you can have my Number Ones if you can get some o' that brilliantine off yourself first."

I was touched. Any sailor's Number One suit, his tiddley suit as he calls it, is his pride and joy, his greatest possession.

I thanked him but refused the offer, saying that I'd be all right. Now it was his turn to be grateful. He looked immensely relieved and grinned hugely, showing big white teeth, then he turned over and went straight to sleep.

A petty officer wearing a decidedly off-white sweater and sea-boots suddenly pushed his way through the survivors and demanded the names of the latest arrivals, ourselves, and details of what ship we were from.

"DEMS gunner eh?" he said to me when I'd given him my name and number. "Soft number that, eh?"

"I miss the rum sometimes," I said, hopefully.

"Some coming up in a minute," he answered.

He winked and passed on to the next man. I liked him. I'd never met a P.O. in such friendly, intimate circumstances. Apart from the Daddies of the training establishment who were of course very helpful and friendly, the only other petty officers I'd had to do with were those minor deities of Devonport Barracks, the hard, leathery, unsympathetic little gaitered men, or the elephantine chiefs as remote as Dr. Johnson. They were all tough and cynical, laughing at jokes we recruits didn't understand.

I decided to try to get some of the fuel oil off myself and made my way to the washroom. I passed Colin crouched under a mess-table, whimpering like a dog. The washroom flat was full of steam and dark bodies and the deck was slippery with oil and soapy water. I stripped and began to scrub under one of the showers, managing to get most of the oil off, though my hair still felt sticky. It was not until I had cleaned myself that I discovered the big bruises all over my legs and body. I must have collected them when I was buffeted along the *Vesta's* deck. Now they seemed to hurt, partly with the scrubbing, I supposed. My legs had a few cuts but apart from these and the bruises I was all right. Things could, as Michael O'Neil had said, have been much worse.

A hairy body shambled towards me through the steam and a face like an ape of hell's leered into mine.

"Told yer she'd break er' bleedin' back, didn't I?"

The bos'n's domino teeth flashed through the steam. But I was not afraid of him now. He was a ghost that had been laid for good and all.

"Yes, but you were wrong. Somebody broke it for her," I laughed back at him, full of goodwill towards my defeated enemy.

He slapped me on the back with a big hairy paw.

"'At's right, boy, but it did the trick all the same," he grinned.

My good humour did not last long, however, for there were

no towels and no dry clothes to put on. To put cold, wet, oil-soaked trousers and jersey on a hot, steaming body is a loathsome experience and I went back to the mess-deck feeling much worse and wishing I'd never thought of having a shower. These were the early days before escort ships carried sacks of spare gear for survivors and the only stuff available was that given or lent by the crew.

The P.O. was just coming down the ladder carrying a fanny, or metal can, full of rum. He shouted:

"Up spirits!"

Then under his breath added the traditional blasphemy:

"Stand fast the Holy Ghost."

The tot which I drank made me feel heady but warm and glowing inside. I breathed strong rummy fumes at Colin underneath the table. He smiled miserably up at me, but refused to come out. I watched the Fiver's sleeping face and wondered if he had been given morphine. The lascars had not stirred and Colin was now shaking his head vigorously as the cook waved his rum under the boy's nose.

There were two other DEMS gunners among the survivors: one was a Canadian, the other a small, secretive Welshman. The former had been on the Norwegian ship, the latter on some general cargo packet. There were in all nearly eighty survivors on the corvette, besides her crew of sixty. Some men from another ship were crammed down in the chiefs' and petty officers' mess. I wondered what it would be like trying to get some sort of meals for us all as we were still some days from the U.K. and likely to be hungry before then. I was hungry now. I was also afraid of what would happen if this ship were hit by a torpedo. In the fo'c'sle we should be drowned like cats in a sack. I was just contemplating the horror of such a situation when the petty officer reappeared.

"Volunteers to help to man a tanker what's copped a packet but 'asn't sunk," he announced in a loud voice.

Everyone stared blankly at him, the third mate asked him what it was all about.

"Dunno," said the P.O., scratching his head with a pencil, "Looks like some sort o' salvage job. Might be some money in it for you merchant fellers, I shouldn't wonder."

The third engineer jumped off the mess-table where he had been sitting swinging his short legs.

"I'll go," he volunteered.

"Good," said the P.O. "Name, rank and ship, please?"

He wrote them down.

"Count me in," said the third mate.

The P.O.'s pencil was busy. A tall young Norwegian raised his hand also. The petty officer seemed to have difficulty in spelling his name. Baines, the bos'n's mate from the *Vesta* and an A.B. I didn't know very well both put their hands up and had their names taken. Nobody else offered to go.

"Well, that might be enough," said the P.O. "Oh, half a minute though, they want a gunlayer. Can't spare any ratings from my department. We're understaffed as it is."

He grinned as he used the words "department" and "understaffed." He looked dirty and tired and I wondered how many days it was since he had had a proper meal or a wash. The Canadian G.L. stared down at his feet, the little Welshman, also a gunlayer, looked furtive and said nothing. The petty officer disappeared through the doorway blackout canvases and the Canadian drawled :

"Volunteer for F.A."

The petty officer returned.

"Cap'n says one o' you gunlayers *has* to volunteer," he said, "So which one of you is it to be?"

He stood looking round at the three of us, his pencil poised, the point licked ready to write down the name, number and ship of the volunteer. The two gunlayers didn't speak or move. I felt uncomfortable and broke the silence :

"I'm not a gunlayer, but I've been acting as one on my ship. I'm only a seaman-gunner really. Will I do?"

The petty officer's sharp eyes snapped in my direction.

"Suppose so," he said. "Name, number and what ship you were on?"

I gave him the details and he wrote them down quickly.

"No next-of-kin, I hope?" he said with unsmiling humour.

He collected the six of us together and led the way out on deck, into the cutting wind. Alongside the corvette was a ship's boat with a dozen men in it. We climbed down a scramble-net and joined them. I shuddered as I felt once again the uneasy motion of a small boat. What sort of mad caper was I in for now? Why had I allowed myself to be embarrassed into volunteering for a job like this, when I could easily have pretended to be sick? It seemed as though in this unreal night one part of me had stood aside and watched the other half doing the most improbable things.

The men in the boat greeted us heartily enough and we pushed off from the corvette's side, but did not put out oars at first as the ship was going to tow us. As we ploughed along in the wake of the vessel the tanker-captain told us the story. His ship had been torpedoed and the crude oil in the forward tanks where she had been hit, had caught fire. They abandoned ship, but the captain had the fixed idea that she would not sink. He and his crew had been picked up by a destroyer but when he asked for volunteers to re-board the stricken vessel only eleven men came forward. The destroyer had then contacted the corvette, handed over the boat containing the twelve men and pushed off. The tanker-captain had then asked for volunteers from among the corvette's survivor-passengers, and here we were. There were now eighteen of us, the minimum skeleton crew needed to work the tanker which, I gathered, was a big one. There had been an original crew of sixty against the *Vesta's* forty-odd men.

The moon peeped out from behind a cloud and we had for an instant a glimpse of a huge hulk not very far away on the port side.

"Oars," said the captain.

We unshipped oars and without a word, as if our mission were secret, someone on the corvette cast us adrift. The ship then put on speed and disappeared into the darkness. We pulled for the tanker and I was glad of the exercise which warmed my body a little.

As we drew near the vessel and rested on our oars, a sight met my eyes which made me numb with terror. The foredeck of the ship was ripped up into a hole thirty feet wide, torn open like a paper bag. A few flames and sparks still licked and jumped about the opening but it was not these that alarmed us : it was the position of the tanker in the water. She was sunk so low in the bows and foredeck that it looked as if she was settling down. The idea of boarding a ship in such a condition seemed preposterous and even her captain stared aghast.

"My God," he breathed at last, "I didn't think she was as bad as that."

The wind whistled through the rivet holes and loose pieces of deck plating clanged together as the sea rushed into the mighty wound made by the torpedo. This alone was a terrifying part of the experience as I found when I shut my eyes to keep out the appalling sight of the torn ship. I began to feel freezing cold and sick; my knees banged together uncontrollably as we sat huddled together in the boat, not talking for some minutes.

"What now?" a voice asked humbly from somewhere in the stern.

"Can't attempt to board her until daylight—if she's still afloat then," the captain answered. "We'll just have to lay off until then, so let's pull round to the lee side, but not too close. Don' want to be sucked under if she founders."

We put the oars in the water and pulled round to the other side of the ship. Once again I was glad of the warming exercise though it did not last long. I soon grew cold when we hove to round on the leeward side of the vessel. I seemed to be the only one in wet clothing. It was better on this, the starboard beam partly because it was sheltered, to some extent, from the cold wind, but chiefly because we couldn't see the hole in the ship's side and watch the sea rushing in and out of it. We sat for perhaps an hour, smoking, pulling a little to keep the boat from drifting, talking hardly at all. Suddenly O'Neil shouted :

"A ship ! It must be the corvette."

He pointed over the starboard gunwale and we peered into the darkness, but could see nothing. The third had been renowned in the *Vesta* for his prodigious eyesight.

"Are you sure, Three Mates? I can't see her myself," said the captain.

I had never before heard a third officer addressed as "Three Mates" and it struck me as funny, even at the time.

"Yes, sir," Mr. O'Neil replied, "only I'm not so sure it is the corvette now. It looks smaller. Shall I give her a flash?"

"All right—if you're sure she isn't a U-boat."

Once more I sat waiting to see if a ship in the night was one of ours, or one of theirs. It turned out, luckily, to be one of ours, an armed trawler patrolling that area, nothing to do with the convoy escorts. It was quite fortuitous that she should have been at hand and we were lucky that her commanding officer had spotted the tanker and was coming to investigate. As they hauled us aboard I remember thinking : this is the maddest night I've ever lived through—if I live through it.

The captain explained to the trawler's commander, an R.N.R. lieutenant, why we were hanging about the wreck in a small boat and the officer agreed to stand by the tanker for the rest of the night and see if she was fit to board when daylight came. It was now four in the morning and would be light in about three hours. We were split up and distributed about the various sleeping quarters of the little ship. I found myself in the small, neat mess belonging to the petty officers; with me were Baines and the other A.B. whose name, I now remembered, was Sleeman, and the old Norwegian. There were four tidy bunks and a small mess-table. A stoker P.O. jumped off his bunk as we came down the ladder.

"Here y'are, lads, 'ave a kip on these for an hour or two," he said in a warm Yorkshire accent.

The other three flung themselves down on the bunks at once, after kicking off their seaboots. I looked at the inviting top bunk with its clean blankets and curtains. Yes, it even had curtains. Then I looked at my clothes. I shook my head.

"Get that there wet gear off an' I'll dry it for you. You can put this on meanwhile," the petty officer said in a fatherly voice, handing me a clean, dry boiler suit with blue and white stoker P.O.'s badges on the arms.

I got out of my wet, filthy trousers and jersey, rubbed myself down with an old towel and put the overalls on. They were warm and dry, wonderful. I felt as grateful as a stray dog taken in on a wet night as I climbed into the upper berth and lay down. The P.O. took away my clothes and came back with a bottle of whisky and some enamel mugs. He poured out about half a mugful each and handed them to us. The big Norwegian drank his as if it were a nursery drink, then turned his face to the bulkhead and went to sleep.

"Ain't you afraid o' copping a packet on one o' these little things?" Baines asked the P.O.

"Never think abaht it," the stoker answered, dragging on a cigarette. "They keep away from us, you know. No, they don't reckon much to us. We carry too many gash-bins for their fancy."

He meant depth-charges. In the light of the morning I saw them, dozens of them, on the deck, in throwers and stowed in all available spaces. The ship seemed to be bogged down with them. Armed with these and a couple of good guns—besides an Asdic set of course, these little ships which were once peaceful fishing vessels looked anything but peaceful now and were most unpopular with U-boats. I felt warm and secure on hearing the Yorkshireman's re-assuring words, but my recent liquid diet of fuel oil, salt water, and rum did not seem to combine well with the strong neat spirit I was now drinking. I suddenly wanted to be sick and, fearful of spoiling the P.O.'s mess, hurriedly left my bunk, rushed up the ladder on to the deck where I leaned far out over the ship's side. After that I felt better and went below to sleep for a couple of hours.

At seven bells, 7.30 a.m., we were given a cowboy's breakfast of bacon and beans. This was washed down with strong tea, "wet" in the naval manner: one handful of tea, one of sugar, one tin of milk, pour boiling water on the mixture and stir vigorously. This is the process known as "wetting."

I changed back into my own clothes which, although dirty, were now dry, then followed the others on deck. The tanker was still afloat. I had hoped that she might peacefully sink in the night so that we could stay on this comfortable, safe little ship until she finished her patrol. But no, we were to attempt a boarding of the tanker at nine o'clock.

XI

IT WAS a fine fresh morning and cloudless. The big tanker wallowed in a slight swell and we could now see part of her screw sticking out of the water as we pulled towards her. We came up alongside the foredeck and I stepped aboard the tanker to make the boat fast to the ship's rail. The others stepped aboard after me, the captain and officers first inspecting the deck damage then making straight for the bridge which towered above us. The engineers went down to the engine-room and while Baines took the seamen off somewhere I wandered aft along an enormous flying-bridge which spanned the main deck, to look at the guns.

As I neared the crew's quarters, situated aft on this new type of tanker, a small black kitten appeared, walking with short, precise steps towards me. It stopped, arched and stretched itself with a miniature elegance, then began to strop itself against my seaboot. I picked the little cat up and stroked it, pleased to make the acquaintance of any living creature on this ghost of a ship. I took the kitten along to the galley, found a tin of milk and gave it some, then I climbed up the after-boat-deck ladder to my department.

The m.v. *Marseillaise* bristled with guns. Her main weapons, a 6-inch surface and 3-inch H.A. gun were both modern, British and familiar to me, but the secondary armament—apart from two Hotchkiss machine guns I found later on the bridge—were not. Mounted above the boat-deck in separate turrets were four machine-guns, .5 calibre, French, and of a type I'd never even heard about. There was a 20 mm. gun, anti-aircraft, also French, and a bomb thrower. The latter I'd seen before but never used. In fact I couldn't believe anybody would ever dare to use one. It was a crude piece of machinery shaped like a big flit-gun with the drum at the bottom. Mounted on a stand, it was made to swivel in a full circle and to tip forwards and backwards. Handles stuck out at the sides of the drainpipe barrel and on the right hand one was a squeeze trigger. You were supposed to point or lay the thing by moving the handles, and so of course the barrel, in whichever direction was required. It worked with either compressed air or steam. Your number two took the safety pin out of a Mills bomb and dropped it down the barrel, mortar fashion, that is if he wasn't too excited and dropped it on the deck, you pointed the drainpipe muzzle at the target—very low-flying aircraft—and squeezed the trigger. If the bomb didn't get stuck at the bottom of the barrel and provided the steam or air pressure was correct, the missile would be hurled about fifty yards and would explode in flight somewhere after that. But if the pressure was low for some reason, then the bomb would simply plop out of the muzzle, land at your feet with the safety pin out and within a few seconds blow you dead—if you hadn't seen it and lobbed it over the side.

All this was explained in detail by a gunnery instructor in
Devonport Barracks and I remembered now the relish with which
he told us. When he had finished his sadistic lecture he invited
questions and someone asked him if it wouldn't be more noble
for DEMS gunners to die by *enemy* action, he replied :

"Well, it don't really matter. So long as they dies somehow it
don't really matter 'ow."

As I stood on the boat-deck of the *Marseillaise* looking up at
the turret which housed this fearsome gadget, I heard a curious
hissing sound coming from it. Nervously I mounted the ladder
and peeped over the side of the turret. Steam was escaping from
a leaking valve underneath a metal box. I climbed in quickly and
tried to turn the valve off but it was stuck. I touched the box
and found that the sides were very hot. I flicked up the lid and
looked inside : one dozen Mills bombs very neatly arranged in
separate compartments, like eggs, like brown chocolate Easter
eggs. I didn't know if it was dangerous to warm bombs or not,
but taking no chances I whipped off my lifejacket and using it
as a sort of oven cloth, picked up the box and chucked it far over
the ship's side. Splash.

After that I fiddled with the point fives, managed to get some
idea of how they worked and where the belts of ammunition were
stowed, then I went along to the bridge to report the condition
of the guns, as I'd been told to do.

Everyone was in the luxurious saloon 'midships. Captain Andrews was seated at the head of the table listening to the reports
of the two engineers, one of them the original chief engineer of
the *Marseillaise,* the other Mr. Evans, third engineer of the *Vesta,*
The chief was saying that the pump-room was badly damaged
and that owing to the forward tilt of the engines it would be
difficult for the oil to circulate. Moreover, the propeller was not
fully submerged. However, they thought they could get us under way in a couple of hours, though the going would be slow.

"Good," said the captain. "Well now, the compasses are out
of adjustment and the bridge is covered with crude oil, but I
think we can manage at our end, eh Mr. Mate?"

He glanced at a tiny chief officer who must have been the small-
est mate afloat. This officer made a midget gesture of assent. The
captain then looked at me.

"Well, Gunner?"

"The guns are all in a firing condition, sir, with ammunition
in ready-use lockers."

(I didn't tell him about the bombs I'd slung overboard).

"Good."

"There's only one thing, Captain."

"Yes?"

"Who's to man the guns, besides myself?"

The captain stroked his chin. He had a long, solemn face like an Easter Island rock sculpture. Stroking it downwards made it seem longer. Mr. O'Neil stepped forward.

"I'll act as his number two, sir," he said.

"Thank you, Three Mates," Captain Andrews nodded.

There was a radio officer who knew how to use the French point fives, the Norwegian, Arnulf Johansen, had been in the gun's crew of his tanker, Baines and Sleeman had been gunners, so we should be able to scratch along if the need arose. I hoped it wouldn't.

"Right," said the captain; "I'll send a signal to the trawler asking her to stand by until noon, by which time, gentlemen, I hope we shall be under way. Oh, incidentally, I think it would be a good idea if we used the after dining-saloon, that is, the engineers' mess. There is only one sure means of escape if the ship sinks and that is one large raft on the port side after-boat-deck. It should support—well—most of us. And by the way, there will be no officer distinction as regards dining. We eat together, one big family, except for those on watch. All right?"

We "aye, ayed" and stood up. It all sounded very cosy, very matey, apart from the bit about the raft. I had noticed that all the boats had been used and that the falls were dangling about six feet from the water. I hoped that if we got hit I wouldn't jump and slide down one, forgetting that there wasn't a boat underneath. It puzzled me that Captain Andrews hadn't mentioned the boat we had used in the night and that same morning. I asked Baines about it. He said that he'd had orders to secure its painter astern so that we could tow it, once we got under way. But, he said:

"It'll sink. They allus does if you tows 'em for any length o' time an' there's a sea runnin'."

Perhaps the captain had anticipated this, but in that case why didn't he have the boat hauled inboard? Baines didn't know. He didn't seem to care.

"Won't matter much if we get the 'ammer. Won't none of us 'ave much of a chance," he said indifferently.

I went gloomily aft. The captain had said that three forward tanks were flooded and that the ship was drawing about thirty three feet forrard. She was so well down by the head that the fore-deck was constantly awash. Another torpedo would be the end of the *Marseillaise*. She would sink like a stone dropped in a pool of blazing oil. The image stuck in my mind although I knew it wasn't a particularly apt one. What was also very worrying was knowing that we might not even need a torpedo to sink us. We weren't going to use the after saloon and be a big happy family for democracy's sake only. The point was that if the ship started to sink rapidly by the head we should be in the last part to be above water and might just have a chance of launching the raft. I went to look at the raft again. It would hold about a dozen, I reckoned. There was a quick-release gadget and and axe to cut the rope which held it if that failed. One slash at the rope and the raft would slide into the sea. We would then jump the forty feet from the boat-deck into the drink after it, some could climb aboard the raft, and the rest would have to hang on to the grablines round its sides. I shuddered at the thought of floundering about in the icy water, left the boat-deck and went below to the crew's quarters.

These were situated just above the water-line but below the engineers' cabins which were all on deck. I noticed that the titles of the engineers were printed above their respective doors in Danish, and thought this strange until later when I discovered that the m.v. *Marseillaise* was in fact built in Denmark only the year before. She had been captured somewhere by the Vichy French and later taken from them by the Free French who handed her over to Britain under the name they had given her, which was her present one. This was her first voyage under the Red Duster and she had been to Galveston, Texas, for her cargo of oil, and had for some reason called at one of the West Indian ports on the homeward journey.

The crew's quarters were dark and eerie, with doors swinging on squeaky hinges and timbers creaking and groaning as the ship rolled gently in the swell. There was not just one mess-deck as in a British ship's fo'c'sle, but a wide companionway with two, three and four berth cabins leading off it—an admirable arrangement.

I entered one of the dark cabins and unfastened the deadlight over the port. Sunshine streamed into the place, revealing an almost clichéd *Mary Celeste* scene: half-empty mugs of cocoa, fag-ends and a scattered pack of cards on the little mess-table, boots and shoes lying about, locker doors open, bedding flung aside on two of the four bunks, altogether an atmosphere of hurried abandonment, but with no *Mary Celeste* mystery about *that* abandonment. I opened one of the clothes lockers and helped myself to some cigarettes which were in there. I opened another one and jumped back in horror as four grisly objects rolled out and thudded, one after the other, onto the deck. Human heads! I looked at them more closely and was relieved to find that they were only faces carved out of cocoa pods—souvenirs from the Indies. I laughed aloud and stuffed the objects back in the locker among the dirty shirts, underpants, ties, socks, photos, condoms. Why "condoms" anyway? Did the word come from condominium, meaning joint rule? I supposed it could, just possibly. I slammed the locker door and left the cabin.

I searched all the other cabins out of sheer curiosity and with great delight, feeling like a pirate, or perhaps only a sea-going burglar. I looked at suits of clothes, pictures of girl-friends, wives, children, mums, dads, and dirty pictures. I looked in lockers, opened drawers, sniffed at bottles, read old letters, browsed through books, played a record—which didn't remind me of anything—on somebody's portable gramophone. Then in one locker I saw a syringe, a box of tablets and something in a bottle, besides an article which I took to be a catheter. For some reason I had the idea that this medical miscellany had been owned by a man with some venereal disease and with an almost superstitious horror I rushed out of the cabin, along the companionway, up the ladder and on to the boat-deck where I stopped to breathe the clean, cold air—and reflect that perhaps the poor fellow only had asthma, or catarrh, or even a sore throat after all.

By seven bells there came the first signs of life from the engines and by noon we began to move ahead slowly, the ship seeming to come to life by degrees, like a person who has been in a coma. The trawler gave us a few salutary blasts on her siren and we boomed back a reluctant farewell, then she steamed away on her patrol, leaving us to fend for ourselves as best we might. The chief steward had cooked up a stew and I went along to the engineers' saloon to try some. It was burnt and tasted foul. When the steward went back to the galley to get some more I nipped out on deck and emptied mine over the side.

"You've soon finished that," he said on his return, eyeing with satisfaction my empty plate.

"Yes. It was very good. Quite, er—tasty," I lied.

"Have some more?"

"No, thank you," I answered, perhaps a shade too hurriedly, for he looked up suddenly and I had to add "The old stomach won't take too much food yet. Swallowed too much oil lately."

He relaxed.

"Glad it's turned out all right. It's a long time since *I* did any cooking."

He said this proudly, as if cooking were too menial for one of his calling. He was an aristocrat of catering, a ship-seneschal, an ocean-going major-domo, an emperor of chop, a mandarin of chow. Cooking, under normal circumstances, was the task of slaves.

"It's fugginorrible," muttered Baines bluntly, tasting the stew.

The chief steward splashed happily in his own stuff and didn't hear him. The second officer of the *Marseillaise*, a tall, prematurely bald, black-bearded man was sitting opposite me.

"Are you a matelot?" he suddenly asked.

"Yes," I said, wondering what had prompted such a question from one who ought to have known the answer.

Two Mates stirred his stew thoughtfully, then said :

"I've buried hundreds of you fellows."

I nibbled bread and considered this remark.

"Were you a naval undertaker?" I asked, not knowing whether there was such a thing.

Weren't sailors always sewn up in their hammocks with two firebars, then slid from under the Union Jack over the side, with the chaplain, among other ship's people, in attendance?

The second mate roared with laughter, then stopped abruptly.

"No. I was first-lieutenant in a destroyer," he explained, "Till six months ago. Lost an eye at St. Nazaire and the Navy gave me the sack."

He pointed to his left eye and I saw that it was glass.

"That's where I buried all the matelots," he added, and I supposed he meant St. Nazaire, "and later I joined the Merchant Service."

He sighed. I murmured condolently. There was nothing else we could do. The second officer's conversation was always rather Hamletan, vague and inconsequential. I suspected that he was slightly dotty, say about south-south east.

I excused myself as soon as I could and went forward to see how the bows were standing up to it now the ship was under way. The captain was looking apprehensively down from his bridge at the fore-deck as I pretended to examine the starboard Hotchkiss. He turned towards me.

"Well, Gunner, what do you make of her?" he asked.

I was flattered that he should consider my opinion at all, but realized that it was only extreme worry which had made him want reassurance from anybody, however young and green. I looked over the bridge windbreak at the great gap in the fore-deck. The sea crashed into it and flooded right over the other side to pour voluminously away down the starboard scuppers. The torn plating was being wrenched to and fro with a sickening sound and the bows shuddered every time a wave smashed into them.

"I think she'll just about hold together, sir, till we get in," I said, not very convincingly I'm sure but Captain Andrews clutched at my straws of words.

"Yes, yes," he cried excitedly. "Yes, so do I !"

Embarrassed by this enthusiasm I went into the wheelhouse

where O'Neil, acting as quartermaster, had just finished his trick and was handing over to Arnulf the Norwegian.

"She's pulling to port, about five degrees," he was saying, "So make an equivalent allowance to starboard."

"Yah," said Arnulf simply.

The bridge had been cleaned up considerably but there was still a lot of oil about, even in the wheelhouse, and walking would have been extremely difficult and dangerous had not somebody had the bright idea of spreading old German and Italian flags on the decking. They soaked up some of the oil and brightened the place a bit especially the huge swastika in the wheelhouse, with its black, red and white markings. We all felt this was symbolical, this trampling of our enemies' colours under foot. It became the custom for every man entering the wheelhouse to spit contemptuously on the flags at their feet. If anyone is puzzled by the presence of these flags on the ship at all, he must be reminded that all ships carry flags of all nations. These are hoisted, usually on halyards amidships, to prove the friendship and courtesy of the vessel towards the nation whose port she is about to enter.

Mr. O'Neil nodded to me as he went off to sample the chief's burnt stew. I stood regarding the tall Norwegian seaman standing with his feet planted firmly apart, at the wheel. His big hands were folded loosely over two of the spokes, his face a mask of calm indifference. I admired his coolness, or the mask.

"What do you think about it, Arnulf?" I asked jerking my head towards the fore part of the ship.

He shrugged his shoulders lightly and answered:

"Do not think about it anything. Not good to vorry. Only vish I vos dronk in Glasgow."

He sighed.

"Perhaps you will be in a few days' time," I said.

"Three Maids say about five or six days at this speed," he answered.

Inwardly I chuckled at his version of Three Mates, but five or six days! This news rocked me as I'd thought of only two or three. We must be moving very slowly indeed and the excessive vibration of the engines, together with a head wind had deluded me into thinking we were doing six or seven knots when in fact we were just managing three, as O'Neil informed me when I saw him a few minutes later throwing his stew over the stern.

"Just think," he said, 'if you were holy you could walk home faster."

I wished I were holy, a wave-walker like Christ or Peter or the old man in Frank Harris' Tolstoian story. The afternoon dragged painfully. I had found a spare telescope in the gunner's cabin and with this kept a good lookout from the 3-inch gun turret, sweeping the horizon in a 180° arc, then pausing to rest my eyes before examining it more carefully in a slow scan. At four o'clock the boat we had in tow filled with water, the tow rope parted and the boat sank gunwale deep. I phoned the bridge and reported the incident. Nobody seemed to mind; it was expected. But I was even more determined to keep near the raft when darkness fell.

In this latitude it began to grow dark at about six. I got some tea and biscuits from the galley and took them back up to my watch tower. I looked for periscopes until I could see one on every wave. It grew darker and darker until I could see nothing but the stars and a faint glow of our wake, then I went off watch.

Those who were not on watch had come aft and were pacing the boat-deck talking quietly. I joined them, but we were all too tired to keep up the exercise for long. The strain of the previous two nights was beginning to tell on us, so we got mattresses and bedding from the crew's quarters, ranged them on the port side of the boat-deck near the raft, and flung ourselves down on them. Someone had found a large tarpaulin boat cover and this we used as a communal bedspread, lying altogether underneath it like a large family of children in a fairy tale.

Arnulf disdained such cowardly sleeping arrangements, however, and slept by himself aloof, unperturbed snug under a mountain of bedding in one of the cabins below decks.

On this, our first night aboard the *Marseillaise,* we were all racked with nerves—except Arnulf who seemed not to have any. Every time the engine-room door clanged as it did when the watches changed, we all sat up quickly, stared wildly into the darkness then lay down again, huddling under the blankets and tarpaulin. I lay in that distressing state when the body is tired out but the mind too nervously alert to let it sleep. Flat aback, I stared at the stars in the cold March sky : at the brilliant Pole Star and stretching above it the Great Bear and Plough; the Herdsman could be plainly seen and below the Northern Crown, Hercules; the Swan, the Dragon, the Little Bear, Cepheus, Cassiopeia, Perseus, Andromeda, the Charioteer, the Bull, the Pleiades. I watched them all, my mind confounded with the recent events which were now kaleidoscoped and presented themselves to me in image-patterns of burning tankers, explosions, startled faces with frantic eyes staring out of them, and Snowflake rocket displays. At last, listening to the engines' throb and the snores of Baines who was sleeping beside me, I fell into a deep and dreamless sleep.

Just before dawn was streaking the western sky I awoke and dragged myself out from under the tarpaulin. Several men were still sleeping so I tried not to disturb them. Watches had changed since I had slept and Baines's place was now occupied by Slee-man. I made my way aft to the 3-inch gun turret and took up my dawn watch there, scouring the horizon through my gun telescope from port to starboard, then slowly back again, star-board to port. It was a red, dangerous dawn. Soon the wind got up and tortured the clouds, twisting and combing them into fan-tastic shapes. It kicked the caps of the waves so that a thousand periscopes seemed to break the sea's face. I kept up this submarine watch for two hours then, nerve-racked, went to break my fast in the galley. The bearded second officer was in there dishing him-self up a huge meal of bacon and eggs, tinned tomatoes and sausages. He looked up as I entered.

"Help yourself Guns, plenty of stuff in the fridge," he said.

I made a fairly modest breakfast for myself and the cat which had been sleeping in the galley but was now awake and washing itself fastidiously. We ate the breakfast by ourselves, the kitten and I, Two Mates having devoured his and disappeared while I was cooking. After drinking innumerable cups of coffee and smoking two of my pirated cigarettes I went forward to see how the bows were standing up to the buffeting they were now get-ting. I stood on the fore-and-aft bridge watching the seas cream-ing over the iron deck beneath my feet, keeping my eyes away from the ugly hole as much as possible. It was difficult at first, like resisting the temptation to stare at a badly disfigured person, un-til I found a distraction in the antics of a trio of porpoises which had unobtrusively come alongside. They pranced and curvetted just off the port beam, racing ahead of us then doubling back, either mocking our slow progress through the grey-green waters, or like dogs just taken out for a run, impatient of their master's lagging steps, yet not wanting to leave him behind. I watched them enviously, thinking that if I could have a wish granted immediately I would choose to be changed into a porpoise and spend my days frolicking in a perpetual game of sea-polo.

That same afternoon a ship appeared on the horizon and I soon recognized it through my telescope as a corvette. It was in fact "our" corvette. Just before dusk it came alongside and I could see the Fiver sitting out on deck, wrapped in blankets with his broken leg sticking straight out in front of him, splinted, and resting on a box. He waved frantically when he caught sight of me on the boat-deck; indeed, so frantic were his gestures that he nearly toppled over. I waved back at him and at others of the *Vesta's* crew. The corvette had come back in search of us for two reasons: to see if we were making progress and to obtain food supplies from our stores. These they reckoned to be well-stocked and they were right, for although it was below decks the dry store had not been penetrated by the sea and we were able to meet the naval vessel's request for sugar, salt, cheese, tinned foods, potatoes, flour and a couple of salted hams. All were transferred willingly—though I noted that the chief steward of the *Marseillaise* did not send anything extra, that is, additional to the items requested—by means of a funicular pulley-arrangement something like a breeches-buoy, but using a hamper. It was too rough for the corvette to come right alongside, or we could have literally handed the goods over to them as our decks were almost level.

"Why didn't you lash the boys up a bit Chief?" I asked the steward when the last basket of stores was dumped on the other ship's deck. "There are tons of fags and spirits in the bond."

The chief steward, good company's man that he was, scowled at me."

"Do you know anything about catering?" he asked.

"No, but——"

"They've got enough provisions to last them a week now, with that lot I've just sent over."

"I wasn't talking about provisions. I said fags and hooch. You're loaded with it and if we go down it goes down too," I answered.

"And if we don't go down?" the steward sneered.

Baines alongside me spoke up :

"You'll write the lot off as damaged stores, square the customs blokes and hustle it ashore one dark night."

He knew the ways of the catering branch too well. The steward flushed hotly.

"I'll report you to the captain," he said turning away.

"Get stuffed," said Baines after him.

It was nearly dark now as the corvette's commander hailed us :

"Thank you for the foodstuffs. We are very grateful. Good luck. See you in the Clyde."

Dusk at sea in war-time is always a depressing hour. We watched the little ship's departure with regret as she sheered off to starboard leaving us all alone on this wide wet sea as she had done once before. Still, she had to land her human cargo safe and sound. It was eighteen lives against two hundred and there was no doubt about the wisdom of her captain's choice, though this did not console us much at the time. It was going to be a black night, the wind was already howling like a fury and the seas were getting bigger. We were on a crippled ship with one inadequate raft. Perhaps we should never see the Clyde. I went aft for a last look-out feeling very gloomy. The chief steward's attitude had shaken me considerably. I'd always imagined that in times of danger men realized their dependence on one another and showed kindness and generosity then if at no other stage of their lives. Most of them do, but some do not, as I found in later, troubled sea-times.

It began to rain. Clearly it would be too wet and windy to sleep on the upper-deck, yet the idea of turning in down below on such a night as this when the ship was in danger of foundering was too fantastic for anyone to contemplate—except Arnulf. He, indeed, seemed not to consider the matter at all, but went straight down to "his" cabin as soon as he came off watch and plunged into the depths of sleep at once, underneath his pile of blankets.

Not made of such Viking stuff I offered to do an extra bridge lookout during the middle watch, from midnight to 4 a.m., the graveyard watch as it is sometimes called, and nobody wonders why. Mr. O'Neil was on the port wing of the bridge when I arrived up there. Sleeman was just relieving Baines at the wheel. the captain was having a short sleep in the chart-room just abaft the wheelhouse and I took up a stand on the starboard bridge wing. I had found a leaky old oilskin in one of the cabins and was wearing this, to my acute discomfort. I had no cap or sou'-wester, the rain was trickling down my neck and but for the fact that I was wearing a belt hitched fairly tightly, would have continued its journey right down into my seaboots.

I stood in this sodden condition for perhaps an hour, peering through a curtain of rain into the darkness as the ship lurched drunkenly into the night. In spite of the shrieking wind it was possible to hear the clang of iron as the loose deck plates thrashed about. Suddenly I heard another noise, a shrill scream from the wheelhouse. I wrenched open the door and found Sleeman draped over the wheel gibbering idiotically :

"She's cracking up ! She's cracking up!"

These were the only intelligible phrases; the rest was verbal surrealism. Sleeman's lips and the corners of his mouth were foam-flecked and he was obviously having a fit induced by extreme nervous tension which had probably been building up for days. Captain Andrews came stumbling out of the chart-room rubbing his eyes, as I was struggling to drag the A.B. off the wheel and keep the ship on the course which was chalked on a little slate hung on the compass mounting. Mr. O'Neil also appeared, attracted by the cries and neither he nor the captain wasted any time asking questions but immediately began to get Sleeman out of the wheelhouse and down to the saloon.

"Take the wheel, Gunner, till I can get a relief up here," the captain ordered.

"Aye, aye, sir," I answered nervously.

I had never held the wheel of a ship before, but this was no time for niceties. In a sweat of terror I felt the ship yawing and swinging in my unksilled hands. It was as though I'd been given a runaway horse to learn to ride for the first time. I felt monstrously put upon, always having to step into some expert's seaboots at a moment's notice. The DEMS should hear some of my complaints when I got ashore. When! I clung desperately to the wheel, trying to keep the ship from swinging to port—the wounded side—by giving her usually too much starboard helm. The result was a gorgeous zigzag which would have confounded any U-boat commander trying to draw a bead on us, but which must have alarmed everyone on board the *Marseillaise*—except Arnulf. However, by the time Baines came blundering and cursing into the wheelhouse I was gradually getting the feel of the wheel and the ship was on a moderately steady course. Baines was naturally not enchanted at having been wakened and told to do another trick at the wheel.

"Whatafugginorrible night," he growled, almost snatching the wheel out of my hands. "Gawd 'elp sailors."

"Amen," I said, and went back to my watch on the starboard wing of the bridge.

I considered Baines. He was typical of the best pre-war merchant seamen : tough, grumbling, good-natured, modest, sea-wise and probably shore-foolish, independent, free, lonely. Yes, life for a merchant sailor was an intensely lonely one, unless he happened to be a company's man in a settled job on one ship. But Baines was not. When he got ashore—if we got the ship in—he would be sent on a fortnight's leave, then he would join the M.N. pool at some big port. He would then sign on a ship full of strange faces and probably leave that for another one at the end of one trip. Perhaps he would team up with another A.B. and they would sign on a new ship together. They might be mates for a year or more, but then they would have to part for some reason and might never meet again. There was something sad and strange about this half-vagrant, lonely life which I too was leading, though only temporarily and for much less pay—for much less work. It bore little relation to service life with its herding yet compensatory factors such as *esprit de corps*, where it existed, or the firm unity, say, of the men on small R.N. ships, or the camaraderie of the Fleet Air Arm which I experienced later in the war.

Somehow we got through the night. When it came light it was obvious that the ship was a few feet lower at the head than she had been the previous day, and we were making much less speed owing to the increased force of the wind. I didn't keep much of a gun-watch that forenoon, reckoning that enemy submarines and aircraft would be too busy looking after themselves to bother much about us, while we in turn were too concerned about the weather to even think of them. In short, we were both fighting our common enemy, the sea.

The storm had blown itself out by evening, leaving a heavy swell which was still extremely dangerous to a ship in such a condition as ours, but not so bad for our spirits as the howling gale. By the time it was dark and those of us not on watch were crawling thankfully under the tarpaulin, the deck was heaving pleasantly and the air not too cold. I fell asleep almost at once, having been awake for the past forty hours. It was one of those good, deep sleeps which seem to last for only a few minutes. Someone was shaking me roughly by the shoulder.

"Wakey, wakey, Guns," a voice said. "The Old Man wants you on the bridge."

It was broad daylight and the radio officer's red face beamed down on me like a sun. I jumped to my feet as soon as I'd freed myself from the tarpaulin. I was glad to have slept so well, right through the real and imaginary terrors of the night. It was like having a bad tooth extracted under gas, but I was worried in case the captain was going to blast me for not keeping a dawn lookout aft. The chief steward's threat to report Baines and myself to the Old Man was, I was sure, only a threat, and one which he dare not carry out. My suspicions were confirmed that day when, after lunch, the steward quietly put a tin of fifty cigarettes on the table beside Baines and I who were the only ones in the mess. We ignored it to show that we were not bought so easily. In any case we already had cigarettes "borrowed" from the deserted crew's quarters.

"After all," Baines rationalized, "we're doin' their work, so we'll smoke their fags."

When I got to the bridge Captain Andrews was studying something in the water, an object a few points off the starboard bow.

"Good morning, sir," I said, as he had not, apparently heard my approach.

"Good morning, Gunner," he answered, not taking his eyes off the object, then handing me his binoculars. "What d'you make of that?"

I trained the glasses onto the thing and focused them to suit my vision. The object seemed spherical, though only about one sixth of it showed as it bobbed occasionally above the surface of the sea. It was black and I thought I could see more than one spike or horn sticking from it.

"Looks like a contact mine, sir," I said, handing back the binoculars. "Shall I shoot it up?"

The captain grinned.

"No reason why we shouldn't have a bit of sport, but don't

open fire until I give the word. Must alter course first and warn them in the engine-room," he answered.

He went into the wheelhouse to give orders to the quartermaster and a warning to the engine-room to expect a big bang. I uncovered the starboard Hotchkiss and fed a metal strip containing about twenty rounds into the receiving side of the chamber. As only one end of the strip was in the gun the weight of the rounds made the strip bend in an alarming manner. I had only once fired a Hotchkiss and it had jammed after three rounds. It seemed to need a number two to hold the cartridge strips up besides feed them into the gun.

The ship swung to port and I waited, slightly tense, for the order to shoot, the mine now being within range at about two hundred yards from us. The captain told me to fire when I was ready so I let go half a dozen rounds, short, and then the Hotchkiss jammed. There was no time to fiddle with it as the mine was already abeam. I left the gun, slid down the companion-ladder handrails and raced along the flying-bridge then up onto the boat-deck to the point fives. I climbed the ladder of the after-most one on the port side, stumbled on the top rung and fell head-first into the turret. The mine was on our quarter now and by the time I'd recovered, made the gun ready for firing and taken aim, the thing was nearly astern, about three hundred yards away.

I opened fire and soon tracers were skimming across the sea in the general direction of the mine. The noise was deafening; this type of gun seemed to make more racket than six Lewis's and was certainly more difficult to shoot. Soon I gave up trying to use the sights and began hosepipe firing, that is, directing the stream of tracers as one would a jet of water. My fifth long burst was successful. There was a dull roar and a thunderous reverberation while a huge column of water mounted high into the air, mushroomed out, then crashed back into the sea. It was a magnificent sight, but I stood even more amazed when hundreds of dead and stunned fish appeared all at once on the surface of the sea and regretted the fact that such a trick could not be performed in a parlour. It seemed a pity, too, that we couldn't pick some of the fish up.

Blessing its efficiency, I cleaned the gun, put the cover loosely over it and went down to get some breakfast.

"Well, that broke the monotony a bit," said Mr. O'Neil as I entered the galley, "Nice shooting, Guns."

"Good weapon," I answered, too modestly, for I was feeling very pleased with myself.

The mine was the first enemy I had personally destroyed in the war. It had been a great pleasure to annihilate an evil object without killing anybody at the same time. Wars should be run on these lines; they would be a pleasant diversion then.

That afternoon some seagulls, possibly attracted in the first instance by the fish we had provided, began to follow the ship. Wheeling and screaming, flirting their feathers and perching on masts and spars, they created a mild form of entertainment for those on watch. I remembered that I had not seen gulls like these since we had left the Canadian and Newfoundland coasts. They were the bigger birds. That meant one thing : land was not very far away. Land, lovely firm-set earth ! My heart leapt for joy as I realized this. I swung the telescope round so that it was directed forrard, over the port bow. Sure enough, there was the faint grey outline of what seemed to be a rugged coast. Wild with excitement I looked again and again to make certain, then I phoned the bridge.

"Land ahead, sir, if it isn't a cloud bank !" I shouted.

The second mate's cool voice answered :

"Sighted it half-an-hour ago, sonny. It's the Butt o' Lewis, the extreme northern tip of the Outer Hebrides—or I'm not a good navigating officer !"

His last words wavered a little, betraying a strong emotion underneath his habitual ex-first-lieutenant's poise. I didn't even mind his calling me "Sonny."

XII

It is sometimes a far cry from sighting land to making a landing, far enough on occasion for the actual landing to produce a feeling of anti-climax.

It was two days after sighting Lewis before we reached our destination in the Clyde and these two days were not entirely free from unpleasant incidents. We entered The Minch at dusk on the day I first saw the Hebridean coastline crucified on the wires in my gun telescope, and started to butt our way south through choppy water between the Outer Isles and the Scottish mainland. I was on watch in the 3-inch gun turret when I heard the sound of an aircraft engine. The phone bell rang and I picked up the receiver with one hand while ripping the breech-cover off the gun with the other.

"Enemy aircraft, bearing green four-five. With H.E., load !" the second mate's words came crisply down the line. "Don't shoot till I give the order. He may not have spotted us."

"But what about some more gunners ? There's only me here," I protested.

I

It was all very well for him to give cool, decisive orders naval-fashion, but I couldn't load, lay, train and fire a 3-inch H.A. gun by myself. Seven was the number required to work the weapon efficiently; three could manage but the firing would be slow.

I slammed a round into the breech and swung the gun round onto a rough bearing, with the noise of the aeroplane engine getting louder. The second officer and Mr. O'Neil came tumbling into the turret, quickly followed by Baines and Arnulf Johansen O'Neil took the trainer's position, Baines stood by to load, Arnulf to supply ammo from the ready-use lockers while the second mate adopted a spotter's attitude, complete with tin hat and binoculars.

We could now see the aircraft from the turret, a dark silhouette against the western sky, as clearly as if it were on a recognition chart: an ME. 110. He had spotted us all right and was turning to make a bombing run in our direction.

"Stand by," said the second officer.

We stood, tense. I watched the dark shape in my cartwheel sight, crawling along a radial wire towards the centre like a wasp on a web. My fingers stiffened on the firing lever while for some unaccountable reason my right buttock began to twitch. I felt like a spider who is afraid of wasps.

"Fire!"

The gun roared and recoiled like a kicking horse. A puff appeared below the aircraft, followed by another and another as we fired rapid. Puffs appeared all round the plane but he came on. Suddenly red and yellowish-white flashes began to show in his nose. I thought at first we had hit him, then I thought he had accidentally switched on his lights—until I realized that the "lights" were 13 mm. tracer cannon shells coming towards us We ducked as some of them smacked against the thick steel turret and whined away into the dusk. As the plane roared overhead the radio officer blazed away at it with one of the point fives— to no great effect either material or psychological, for he didn' score a hit and the airman couldn't see his tracers. We sprang back to our places at the gun but soon dropped down again as three bombs burst astern of us, almost simultaneously, the last very close. Shaken, we resumed our positions and I fired a couple of rounds at the enemy as he began to turn. Both missed and was cursing everything when the second mate ordered me to cease firing. I stared at him for a moment, then he pointed to a speck in the distant sky, not far from the Messerschmidt. It soon grew bigger, and bigger.

"One of ours! A Hurricane or Spitfire. The Jerry's seen him and he's off!" the second yelled.

It was true. The German had abandoned his attempt at a second run on us and was fleeing northwards for his life, the R.A.F. plane close on his tail. Thin shreds of light flickered electrically between the two aircraft. The wicked tracers. Soon the German was a red glow diving down, down into the rough dark waters, and the Spitfire zipping back to his base on the mainland somewhere, doing one slow victory roll as he passed us close by on the port side. We stood silent, dazed and thankful while the captain tried to make four siren blasts sound like gratitude.

Later Captain Andrews gave us large tots of rum in the after-saloon. This freed my numbed mind, allowing it to wander into melancholy, philosophical pastures. With bleared cosmic vision I saw the blazing aircraft diving into the sea as no more than a fag-end flung into a puddle. I wanted to weep for the futility and insignificance of Man. I left the saloon and lurched aft, declaiming to windward some half-forgotten lines from Henry the Eighth;

> *I shall fall*
> *Like a bright exhalation in the evening,*
> *And no man see me more.*

Then I tripped over a tangle of mooring ropes and slept among them till dawn.

Icy rain woke me and drove me to the galley for a stiff drink of ship's cocoa, the only available refreshment. Colly the kitten stropped against my seaboot and I ripped him open a new tin of milk with my knife, wondering for the first time what had happened to Sleet when the *Vesta* was hit. Drowned, I supposed, like many a ship's cat before her. But they saw life, these sea-cats. Sleet had joined the *Vesta* at Liverpool after jumping ship from a South American meat boat which was being fumigated. Before that she had been on the Australian run, the Cook had informed me, though how he knew was anybody's guess. But whatever her sea time she had paid off now, rung eight bells.

I went up to the boat-deck to collect my borrowed oilskin from the gun turret. It was dull and misty. There was no land in sight but I calculated our position to be somewhere just south of Tyree. This later proved correct; we were actually parallel with Iona, having passed the islands of Canna, Rum, Eigg, Muck, Coll and Tyree while I lay asleep among the ropes.

After being on watch for about an hour I noticed that the ship was steering erratically. The second mate came hurrying aft, Baines following. I shouted to the latter:

"What's the buzz?"

"Steering's gone. Must've bin that bomb what just missed us. Shook up the telemotor or somefink," Baines shouted back.

The engine-room telegraph rang twice : stop engines. Life seemed to ebb out of the vessel as the great throb of her heart ceased and I became aware of sounds which had hitherto been muffled : the rush of the sea against our sides, the susurrant wind in shrouds and stays, the scream of gulls. It reminded me of the first morning we had boarded the abandoned ship. The captain came hurrying aft, followed by Mr. Evans, the *Vesta's* third engineer.

"What's the matter, Taff ?" I shouted to the third when he appeared, spanner in hand, from under the poop.

"A break in connections—too technical for you to understand, man," he grinned.

Whatever it was we drifted helplessly all the forenoon and I became apprehensive as land hove in sight when the mist lifted, and I imagined us drifting towards dangerous rocks. The land was apparently the island of Colonsay which meant that we were near the Firth of Lorne. Near the end of the afternoon the damage was repaired and once more we were under way, thanks to the skill of the third engineer. He was obviously a man who needs a crisis to bring out the best in him. Boastful and petty he had seemed on the *Vesta*, yet he had been one of the first to volunteer to board the *Marseillaise* and never showed any sign of fear or hesitation to do his job in the engine-room even at times of extreme danger from underwater attacks.

That night we rounded the Mull of Kintyre, entered the Firth of Clyde and anchored off Arran. It was an uneasy night. When our one anchor began to drag as the wind got up, we had to weigh it for fear of its pulling the bows off. We dare not proceed up the Clyde until daylight, so we spent the night swinging about in mid-firth, unable to seek shelter in the lee of the land as we did not know how many feet of plates were hanging off our bottom and we didn't want to risk getting caught up on the rocks. We were all too excited to sleep—except Arnulf, wondering if we should founder on this, our last night at sea, and so near to our own land that we could have swum ashore. But the good ship, though she was even lower at the bows, weathered the night.

At eight o'clock in the morning, a fine, clear morning, we began to move cautiously up the Clyde. Two tugs came down the river, passed us, turned around and began to follow us. One on either side they began to catch up and finally drew alongside. The captain bellowed at them through a megaphone :

"Thank you, but we do *not*, repeat *not*, require assistance from you."

But the tugmen were not to be done out of a bit of easy salvage money, or so they thought. A deck-hand heaved a line on to us. Nobody made any attempt to catch it and it slithered off again into the sea, so they tried a new gambit. Coming closer alongside the seaman handed up the bight of a 3-inch rope to me, as if it were a personal gift.

"Don't touch it, Gunner!" the captain shouted down.

Hands in pockets I grinned at the tugman who was now swearing furiously and trying to hoop-la one of the bollards with the rope's bight.

"Gunner on the bridge!" Captain Andrews' voice boomed urgently.

I hurried up there and stood panting like a dog.

"Uncover the Hotchkiss and point it at them," he ordered.

I obeyed.

"Now," the captain shouted down at the offending tug, "clear off or you'll get a couple of bursts with this."

He tapped the Hotchkiss barrel significantly. I hoped they wouldn't call our bluff; for one thing I didn't want to shoot up old tugboat in case anyone got hurt, but for another I was sure the machine-gun would jam, in which case we should lose face. However, an angry tugboat skipper now appeared for the first time out of his wheelhouse. He shook his fist at the captain.

"I'll report ye for threatening me!" he shouted, the veins standing out on his forehead with his furious vocal exertion.

"Then go away and be damned to you!" Captain Andrews snapped back at him smartly.

The tug sheered off quickly and was followed, a few moments later, by the other, the hands on their decks philosophically going about other forms of work. I covered the gun and asked the second officer what all the fuss had been about. He explained that if the tug had succeeded in making a line fast to us they might have been able to claim part of any salvage money there might be for the vessel.

"Even if the rope was only on for a few seconds?" I asked incredulously.

He nodded. Even so. The laws of salvage were tricky, very tricky indeed.

The end was in sight. News of our arrival had spread upstream and as we passed ships at anchor, both naval and merchant, the decks were lined with cheering crews while congratulations poured over us through megaphone and loud-hailer. Sirens wheezed, boomed and whooped as we stood on deck, leaning against the rails and waving in a leisurely, faintly languorous, regal manner. Not exactly the conquering heroes, but at least the undefeated. It was a kind of victory.

When we reached our anchorage, just off a small island naval base, the shore was dark with people, cheering and waving. We dropped the hook and the captain summoned everybody to the saloon amidships. A tumblerful of rum was poured out for each man. Captain Andrews raised his glass.

"Gentlemen, to you all, for everything you have done," he said quietly.

We murmured self-depreciative remarks but drank appreciatively and toasted the captain in turn. Then we sat down, smoking and talking with some custom's men who had just arrived on board. I think I drank another half a glass of neat rum.

When I came to my senses, several hours later, I found myself in the galley peeling potatoes and watching, as if through frosted glass the second mate cooking something at the stove.

"What time is it?" I asked thickly, "and how the devil did I get here?"

"It's about four o'clock. I found you wandering about on deck after everybody had gone ashore. Set you to work in here. Hope you don't mind," the second grinned over his shoulder.

"Everybody's gone ashore?"

"Except you and that Norwegian chap—and me. I'm staying till a relief comes in the morning. We've got half a dozen relief seamen on board.

My tongue felt as if it had been licking somebody's seaboots.

"Has no relief come for me, then?" I asked.

"Don't suppose the DEMS people even know you're aboard," answered the second mate, frying unconcernedly.

"Have I your permission to go ashore and tell them?"

He shrugged.

"Better wait till to-morrow. Won't be a boat to-day."

I roused Arnulf from a deep rum-sleep and we had a huge meal with the second, consisting of chipped potatoes, fried eggs, sausages and tinned tomatoes. We played cards all the evening with cigarettes for stakes and afterwards I slept in the gunners' cabin. Next morning Arnulf and I were up early waiting for the boat which would bring the relief for the second mate and take us "to the beach." It came at two o'clock in the afternoon. Impatiently we waited for the second to hand over the ship, then as soon as he was ready we climbed into the launch which took us to the small landing stage near the naval base. We shook hands with the second officer and he went off to an hotel where Captain Andrews was staying with his wife.

"The Navy'll take care of you now," the second had said, nodding towards the R.N. office at the end of the jetty. "Good luck."

Arnulf and I lumbered along the wooden planks in our slow seaboots. The door of the office stood open and inside we could see a Wren typist bent over her machine.

"Woman," said Arnulf, half to himself. "Have not seen for some time."

While he was looking curiously at her, as if she were of another species, I knocked on the door. The Wren either didn't hear or didn't care, for she just kept on typing. I was about to step inside the office when an R.N.V.R. sub-lieutenant swept round the corner and almost collided with me.

"Excuse me, sir," I began, before he got into the hut.

"Yes?"

"We've come from the damaged tanker over there, the *Marseillaise*. This man is a Norwegian merchant seaman. I am a DEMS rating. Could you please tell me where the nearest DEMS base is and how to get there? And my friend would be glad if you could direct him to the place where the rest of his crew is to be found."

I thought that just about covered everything, but the officer looked completely blank.

"You say you are a *what* rating?" he demanded.

"D.E.M.S., sir," I answered.

"Royal Navy?"

Clearly he had never heard of the DEMS branch. I started to explain :

"Yes, sir. The DEMS ratings are gunners on merchant ships. They——"

"Yes, yes, I know," he lied, then appeared to be thinking hard. "But if you're a naval rating what are you doing dressed like that?"

He looked with distaste at my frayed, oily jersey, torn and filthy trousers, burnt seaboots.

"I'm a survivor from the s.s. *Vesta*. We're both survivors. We boarded the *Marseillaise* as part of a volunteer crew," I explained.

"Say, 'Sir'," said the young, commission-conscious officer.

"Sir," I answered.

He looked embarrassed.

"Survivors? Well, I don't quite know what to do with you."

He hesitated, then went on awkwardly.

"You see, it's really my half-day."

It was my turn to look blank. I certainly felt it.

"It's—it's Saturday," the sub. explained, pinking.

Arnulf and I looked at each other. The Norwegian nodded gravely.

"Saturday," he agreed. "Ya."

"Yes, and I'm off duty, you see," said the officer, eagerly, then he remembered to look hurt. "So I can't really help you, can I?"

"No, I suppose not," I said, "unless you happen to know someone who *is* on duty who might be able to tell us where we are to
go."

Be damned to calling this commissioned clothes-horse "Sir."

"Oh, yes, *rather*," he exclaimed. "Just a minute. I think I see
someone over there."

He strode quickly along to the jetty steps where a boat was just
drawing up alongside. Waiting to board it was a big man wearing
a kilt. He had a shotgun under one arm and a brace of rabbits
in either hand. The sub-lieutenant saluted the kilted hunts-
man, said something to him, then turned and beckoned to us.
We walked towards them.

"Follow this officer into the boat," said the sub.

We did as we were bid, watched suspiciously by the two smart
sailors in charge of the launch. The officer stood aloof with his
rabbits and shotgun, staring ahead. I watched the sub-lieutenant
strolling back along the jetty as we sheered off. He looked carefree and happy, now that he had rid himself of us, his half-day
spoilers. One of the matelots in the boat edged towards us and
said to me out of the corner of his mouth :

"You in the rattle, mate?"

"Shouldn't be at all surprised," I answered.

Arnulf lit a cigarette.

"No smoking in the boat," growled the coxswain.

The Norwegian cursed and flung the fag far over the side.

"What's he?" I asked the sailor with the boat-hook, nodding
towards the rabbitter who was now staring at the distant hills in
their early spring beauty, for which I had no eye at the moment.

The matelot made a sign with his fingers on his cuff indicating
two rings and a half, for lieutenant-commander. We were
approaching a large submarine depot ship I'd noticed before
lying out in the bay. I asked the sailor what ship it was.

"Fugginardship," he retorted, preparing his boat-hook for
action by leaping onto the boat's half-decking and doing a series
of physical jerks, or so it seemed.

Three submarines were tied up alongside the mother ship, or
"mumship" as some of the submariners called it. There was great
activity as fuel pipes and torpedoes were being swung aboard
the boats. We followed the rabbits and kilt up the ladder saluting
the quarter-deck as we stepped aboard the depot ship. The "two
and a half" in highland number ones muttered something to a
chief petty officer, jerking his head in our direction. Then he
strode off to the wardroom. I had the sense of being very remotely
controlled. The chief said :

"All right, you two. Down below into the canteen. This way."

We followed, meek as rabbits, along the deck and down a companion-ladder into a spacious canteen where men were playing table-tennis, eating, smoking, playing cards, dominoes and darts. It was a kind of expurgated matelot's Elysium. We passed through the canteen flat watched with indolent curiosity by the relaxed submariners as the chief ushered us into a store.

"Sorry we got no survivors' kit here," he apologized, "but we'll see what we can do."

He turned to the stores assistant.

"Couple o' jerseys, Jack," he said.

The tiffy swung round and back again with two off-white submarine jerseys and slid one towards each of us.

"Now give the poor bastards something to eat. They looks half-starved," the chief grinned.

The S.A. disappeared and then returned with two six pound tins of corned beef which he plonked down in front of us.

"That's it, boys. Up that way now," said the chief, pointing to a vertical steel ladder.

We climbed it and emerged, bewildered, on deck. Arnulf stuck a cigarette in his mouth and lit it.

"Put that cigarette out on the quarter-deck!" a voice rasped.

A thick-set lieutenant stood with his hands on his hips glaring up at the Norwegian.

"Domn!" said Arnulf, and flung the cigarette down at the man's feet.

"Pick that up," the officer snarled.

Arnulf glowered down at him.

"What are you?" the lieutenant said suddenly to me.

"Survivors," I answered, having discovered that this word was something of a Sesame—though it hadn't really opened many doors up to now.

"Oh," said the lieutenant, a little more sympathetically, "What ship?"

I pointed to the *Marseillaise,* not more than five hundred yards distant. The officer nodded.

"That one? Oh, yes, she came in yesterday, didn't she? Well, we'll soon fix you up."

He strode over to the other side of the deck, leaned over the rail without touching it, and shouted something to the men below in the launch, then he turned and beckoned us across. Down the ladder we went and into the boat for the second time. We shoved off and I sat back happily, glad to be away from the floating barracks atmosphere of the depot ship, until I saw that we were heading back to the *Marseillaise.*

"Hey, we want to go ashore!" I shouted to the coxswain.

"Wantin' and gettin's two different things," he answered philo-sophically.

"But we've just come off that broken down bastard!" I stormed, pointing to the tanker.

"Can't help that, mate. Orders," the other sailor said placidly.

I looked at Arnulf who shrugged and lit a cigarette. The mate-lots produced dog-ends from inside their caps and lit up too. Eventually so did I.

"The English, very funny little people," the Norwegian com-mented.

I didn't feel much like disagreeing.

We spent the night aboard the tanker, going to bed early out of sheer boredom. The following morning, Sunday, we decided to try again, so in our new jerseys and with our tinned bully beef wrapped in brown paper we hung about on deck waiting for a passing boat. There weren't many about on Sunday morning, but at last, at about ten o'clock, I spotted a dinghy some two hundred yards off pulling for the shore. We shouted to the rower who altered course and came alongside.

"You take us ashore?" Arnulf asked him.

The man nodded. We climbed into the boat and he pulled for the landing stage. We thanked the man and asked him what time there would be a boat going to the mainland. He shook his head.

"There'll no be one to-day, laddie," he said. "It's Sunday."

"Can you take us, then?" I asked.

"Ah'm afraid not. Ah canna spare the time," he answered.

It would have been a long pull to the opposite shore, more than five miles.

"All right, thanks anyway," I said, as we started off along the jetty.

We sat down outside the R.N. office, the door of which was firmly shut and locked. We just sat and smoked, hopelessly, until after about an hour Arnulf sat up suddenly, then jumped to his feet.

"Boat head this way. Pilot boat, I tink," he said.

I strained my eyes and presently saw a boat with a blue flag coming towards the jetty. We strolled along to the steps and waited for us to come alongside. There were only three men on board. I asked them if they could take us across to the mainland, explaining who and what we were.

"Sorry boys, canna do it," said the skipper, shaking his head.

I conferred with Arnulf. We unwrapped our parcels and showed the man the twelve pounds of corned beef.

"Look," I said, "we're not hungry, are you?"

The skipper took the tins from us.

"Come aboard, boys," he smiled.

So, using bully beef currency, we bought ourselves a ride to Ayrshire, as the skipper told us the place was where he landed us. There was a road nearby and we walked along this in a northerly direction until a country bus appeared behind us, then we stopped it and climbed aboard. I whispered to the conductress :

"We're a couple of shipwrecked mariners. Got no money."

"That's all right, dear," she smiled warmly. "We know how it is. You sit down here."

She showed Arnulf and I to a seat, then spoke to the driver who turned round and grinned.

"All right, boys. We'll soon have ye at Greenock," he said.

It was as though they had been expecting us. We sat back and relaxed in the friendly, country-bus atmosphere. Greenock. I knew there would be a DEMS base in a port the size of Greenock, and Arnulf would be able to contact his shipmates from there. I listened lazily while the conductress prattled in a soft Ayrshire voice, with an enchanting accent. Presently I fell asleep and when I woke up we were in Greenock.

We trudged along the sunless, mid-afternoon streets of the port, looking for Arnulf's M.N. pool offices. They would be shut of course, but to our delight we suddenly met one of the Norwegians walking along towards us. After much jubilation in their own language the two men turned to me and Arnulf said that the survivors who had been on the corvette had all been landed at Greenock and that his shipmates were still there, staying in a hotel. Later they would be going on to Glasgow. He gave me an address of some lodgings where he always stayed when he was in Glasgow, we shook hands and parted, he going off with his friend, I in search of the DEMS base. I was sorry to leave Arnulf Johansen. He seemed to me to be the most reliable kind of shipmate one could possibly wish for, and I sincerely hoped we should meet again.

Feeling cold and depressed I went down to the docks and asked a policeman at one of the gates if he knew of a DEMS base in the port. He pointed to a squat, dismasted, 1890's wooden ship in one of the basins not far from the gate.

"That's your H.Q." said the policeman " 'The Altmark'— that's what your blokes call her."

I thanked him for this cheerful bit of news and made my way towards the hulk from which fluttered a white ensign. I went up the gangway, saluted, and stepped on deck. It was more like being on a vast houseboat, or an ark, than on a ship. No one was on watch at the head of the gangway, but I could see the figure of an officer moving about in what I supposed to be the wardroom. He seemed to be taking tea with a lady. I knocked on the jamb of the open door. The officer, a lieutenant R.N.V.R., turned quite startled, and looked at me.

"Excuse me, sir," I began.

The man stepped past me and shouted down a hatch :

"Chief !"

A red-faced chief petty officer hurried up the companion-ladder.

"Sir?" he gasped.

"See what this man wants," the lieutenant ordered.

The chief gulped some air down then frowned heavily at me.

"Off cap !" he snapped.

I took off my rolled balaclava-helmet which I'd forgotten was still on the back of my head.

"Well?" demanded the chief, "who are yer, and what d'yer want?"

"I'm a DEMS seaman-gunner, Henry Warren, D/JX 214634, from the s.s. *Vesta,* sunk by torpedo, March the sixteenth," I answered.

I wanted to add : I want a bath, a change of clothes, some money, a travel warrant, and fourteen days survivor's leave, but thought it would be rash to ask for so much all at once.

The chief's eye softened. He turned to the officer and repeated my brief history, in the third person. The lieutenant looked puzzled, but not at me.

"Sunk on March the sixteenth? But it's now the twenty-sixth. Where has he been for the past ten days?" he asked the chief.

Staying at the Ritz, I thought. It was like a party game. "Interpreters" one might have called it. I explained that I had helped to salvage a half-sunken tanker, and that it wouldn't go very quickly. When the chief had relayed this intelligence the officer deigned to glance quickly in my direction.

"Oh, well, in that case, see that he gets a bath and fresh clothing, food and a bed ashore if he prefers it. Report him to me at Oh nine double Oh to-morrow forenoon, Chief," he said.

"Aye, aye, sir," answered the Chief, then he turned to me, "All right my son, down the hatch."

I preceded him down the hatch, onto a lighted mess-deck.

"Don't know what he meant about 'fresh clothing'," the chief muttered, "there ain't none here to give yer. We don't keep survivors' gear."

"Where can I get some, then?" I asked, beginning to wonder why anyone bothered to survive.

"Glasgow, I expect," said the chief. "You'll be going there to-morrow. Now then, there's the washroom, and if you'd rather sleep ashore——"

" I would."

"Then see me later and I'll let you have a chit."

"Thanks, Chief."

In the steamy washroom a DEMS gunner was splashing happily in what looked like a huge pie-dish. There were two or three of these baths so I took one, filled it from the hot and cold showers, stripped and flopped into the water. The other man looked in horror at my filthy body, got up, dried and dressed himself in a few seconds and hurried out of the washroom. I scrubbed myself sore for about an hour, but still couldn't get all the fuel oil out of my pores and hair. However, I was a bit cleaner and after I'd dressed I felt a lot better. I got a meal-chit and one for a bed ashore in a canteen.

The canteen women made a fuss over me and I managed to borrow a razor to shave off my tawny doormat of a beard. After a good meal I went to bed in a small cubicle and slept for twelve hours. The next morning I was sent to Glasgow by train and reported to the DEMS offices which were in a large station hotel taken over for the duration of the war by several service departments. I had a note from DEMS Greenock so this saved me the trouble of putting on the record again. Besides, they knew all about the affair. The commander was quite benign.

"Well done, my boy," he beamed, shaking my hand. "And now, as soon as you've got your survivor's kit we'll fix you up with some leave. Chief, see to this man's needs, will you?"

"Yessir," said the inevitable and ubiquitous chief petty officer.

They sent me a long tram-ride away to a billet for DEMS ratings.

"When do I get some kit?" I asked the chief in charge of the place.

"When you get to the place where they dish it out," he answered.

"Not here then?"

He shook his head

"No. Dalmeny."

"Where's that?"

"Dunno. Never bin there."

"Do I go to-day?"

"To-morrow."

"Well, look, Chief. I've no money and I want to send a telegram. Do you think I could go down to the shipping company's offices and collect some of my sixpence-a-day back pay?" I said.

"All right," answered the chief, "here's half a dollar. Have a good time, don't get drunk, and pay me back someday."

I thanked him and set off for town, first calling at a post office to send my people a telegram telling them I hoped to be home in a day or two. With my one and six change I boarded a town-bound tram, intent on storming the *Vesta's* company offices. I found them without much difficulty in a gloomy Victorian building which would have fascinated only a Betjemanite. Everything about the place suggested established prosperity, solidity, dourness. I mounted the stairs and knocked on a thick oak door. No answer. I knocked again. Still nothing. I opened the door and saw an elderly man seated at a large desk.

"Who are you? Why don't you knock before entering a room?" he growled, looking up under thick brows which stuck out like eyeshades.

My knuckles were still stinging from the blows I'd rained on his wretched door. I ignored his second question.

"I was the gunner of the *Vesta*. She was one of your ships, wasn't she?" I said.

"Well, and what if she was?" the man demanded, looking at me with suspicion and distrust.

"I haven't been able to draw any back pay yet and wondered if your company would mind letting me have some. It owes me about two pounds."

"Where's your identification?" he grunted belligerently.

"I haven't any, but if you would be good enough to phone the DEMS office I'm sure they'd vouch for me," I suggested.

"How can they vouch for ye if they canna see ye?" he wanted to know.

His voice rose to a scream and my temper rose with it.

"How the blazes should I know?" I cried.

He jumped up and charged across the room, shaking a big hairy fist and nearly knocking the aspidistra off its pedestal.

"You get out of my office!" he raged, "I've handled hundreds of men like you at sea for years!"

"Between the wars?" I sneered, backing quickly out of the room.

The heavy oaken door slammed in my face and I read the name Captain J. MacIntyre on it for the first time, my eyes now being accustomed to the gloom of the building. A door opposite opened and a younger man came out, dressed in a smart grey suit.

"Can I help?" he asked, smiling.

I put on the record. He listened like the dog on the disc. Finally he said smoothly:

"I'd like to help you, really, but I'm afraid we can't pay you anything until the accounts are completed and the whole crew is officially paid off. I'm sorry."

He smiled a sad, apologetic smile and backed into his office.

closing the door quietly, but firmly. I stood for some moments stroking the stubble on my chin, wondering when I should be able to buy myself a razor to shave it off, then I went back to the billet.

I slept the night at the DEMS place, then next morning was sent by train to Dalmeny, in Linlithgowshire, to a naval stores where I was given some new gear, including a razor and brush. Back in Glasgow by the early afternoon I shaved, changed into a new, ill-fitting uniform, left the rest of my gear stowed at the billet and hurried off to the DEMS offices to get leave.

"Paybook?" the paymaster-lieutenant asked, without looking up.

I boggled.

"Paybook? I haven't got one, sir," I said.

"Why not?"

"It went down with my things on the ship."

The paymaster leaned back in his chair and stared at me.

"You know that you are supposed to carry your paybook at all times, don't you?" he said.

"Yes, but it wouldn't have been very readable, sir. Salt water and crude oil——"

The paybob held up an admonitory finger.

"A waterproof container, that's what you should have had it in. Remember next time."

His Wren assistant handed me a railway warrant, leave-chit and ration card for a fortnight. The paybob gave me one pound. I looked hard at the solitary note.

"Excuse me, sir," I said, "but I have about ten pounds back-pay due to me."

"The balance will be forwarded to your leave-address when a check has been made," he announced without looking up.

The Wren smiled sympathetically.

"Look after your paybook in future," the paymaster added. "Next, Chief."

It was not altogether their faults. It was their desks that were partly to blame, I decided. Stick any man behind a desk and it was like giving him a gun, or for that matter, a car. They were all power symbols, ego-satisfiers, the trappings of brief authority.

I wandered down the long, thickly-carpeted corridor of the hotel, musing on deskocracy and carrying my small brown attaché case in which were my new shaving things, a spare pair of socks and a handkerchief. I passed a poster in the hall which read: TRAVEL LIGHT.

That evening I boarded a southbound train and entered a compartment in which were two R.A.F. groundlings, the only occupants. I spread a newspaper on the opposite seat, then sat down and put my feet up. One of the men looked at my new boots and sloppy uniform, my cap-tally tied in its hasty knot and jerking his head towards me said to his pal in a low, but audible voice :

"Just joined."

The frustrated rage of several exasperating days burst forth. I yanked the airman to his feet and whammed my fist into his startled face. He folded up with a groan and slid between the seats, while his pal gaped in open-mouthed bewilderment.

Feeling that life was much more satisfying when you could hit back at it, I took my case and moved off to find another compartment for the night.

The train rattled southwards.

PART TWO

I

M y n e x t voyage as a DEMS gunner was remarkable only for its placidness. I went on a troopship to Suez via the Cape, taking members of the Wessex Regiment out, bringing Italian prisoners of war back to Durban, and civilian passengers back from there to the United Kingdom.

During this trip we—the R.N.R. gunlayer and myself—lived better than any passengers. We had luxurious accommodation aft, under the gun-deck, including private bathrooms. We had our clothes laundered free and dined in immaculate whites with the second steward, the assistant purser, the dispenser, and other secondary officers of the ship. We had a well-trained crew of merchant seamen and were only obliged to keep dawn and dusk watches ourselves, though we actually spent most of our time on the gun-deck as it was spacious and private, out of bounds to troops, passengers, and of course prisoners. Here, on this most holy of holystoned decks we kept watch, drilled the crew, slept when it was warm, read, sipped lime juice, sunbathed, told stories, shot sharks, dreamed post-war dreams.

It was too good to last. At Avonmouth I was taken off the ship, sent on a few days' leave, then made to do a gunlayer's course for a month in Bristol, as I now had more than the requisite amount of sea-time in to qualify for G.L. training. After the Orient Line's excellent and plentiful cuisine I felt half-starved and grossly overworked on the gunnery course. I emerged a thinner, paler, though much more efficient gunner and was immediately drafted to Cardiff.

There was no DEMS billet in Cardiff at that time and gunners were living individual lives in lodgings, which suited me well. We were given addresses of householders who had been told they were to give board and lodgings to one or two gunners, whether they liked it or not. I was very lucky to get accommodation at the home of a respectable shipyard fitter, so with him, his tidy Welsh wife and nine-year-old son I sojourned comfortably for a month.

It was now the beginning of 1942, a cold, bitter winter with deep snow. I longed for the tropics again and a pleasant, lordly life on some fast trooper. If I'd been holding the Monkey's Paw,

I couldn't have been granted a more fateful wish. I got the tropics, and the trooper, but it wasn't a fast one and the life on board was anything but lordly. The trip was, in fact, benighted from the start.

I was sent to Greenock in charge of seventeen other gunners, all of whom were on draft to ships in the Clyde. Six of us were for one vessel, the m.v. *Astrid,* which puzzled me. Although the DEMS was fast becoming a big organization there were still not enough trained men in it to send six gunners to every ship. Therefore, there must be something special about the m.v. *Astrid,* I thought. There wasn't particularly, but then I did not know that she was a cargo-passenger turned troopship, and that extra DEMS gunners were now sent to all ships carrying troops. I had observed with some repugnance that the DEMS was becoming more "pusser" as it got bigger—that is to say, more naval routine and discipline were creeping into it. Men going into the Navy were in some cases herded straight into the DEMS without being given the chance to volunteer for this branch. More and more soldier-gunners of the Royal Maritime Regiment were manning the merchant navy's weapons, while more Royal Marine and Royal Navy reservists, together with many of the early volunteers, were being taken off the ships and used as instructors in shore bases. I was looking round for some as yet undisciplined branch of the Navy to which I might possibly transfer. The new Royal Naval Commando sounded interesting but too arguerried, too aggressive for my nature. Besides, it was already a highly disciplined corps and I was looking for something more desultory, an unorganized body where few obeisances were wanted and there was plenty of leisure-time to cultivate one's fancies of the moment, for, I had decided, it was going to be a long war and I might as well settle down peacefully to enjoy it.

We arrived at Greenock thirteen hours late, the train having been held up by snowdrifts, frozen points and the usual muddle at Crewe. I handed over the draft-chits to the same chief petty officer on the same prison-hulk of a vessel I had reported to as a survivor the previous year. He didn't recognize me. The six of us for the *Astrid* were told she was out doing trials and that we should have been on her. As we had arrived late we had missed her departure that morning and now we should have to live on "The Altmark" for two or three weeks. We all groaned loudly as soon as the chief had gone, but there was nothing else for it. We hurled our bags and hammocks down the hatch and slid down the ladder handrails after after them. Accommodation was cramped, food was poor, the weather was foul, the duties tedious and the extra gunnery instruction superfluous as we had all just had nearly two months' intensive training at Bristol and Cardiff

Moreover, Greenock was a boring place to be in when it was under eighteen inches of snow. Most places are.

We were elated when towards the end of January we were ordered to Glasgow to join our ship, but not so keen when we saw it. There was a Royal Marine Corporal and one Seaman Gunner already on board, so including ourselves there were eight gunners all told. The four of us who wore new G.L.'s badges were to man an Oerlikon 20 mm. apiece, while the three seaman-gunners and the corporal who was senior gunlayer, together with any of us who were off watch, were to form the crews of the 4-inch and 12-pounder. It didn't seem a very satisfactory arrangement and I said so to George, the corporal, suggesting that we should ask for a few troops to make up the 4-inch and H.A. gun's crews, while we Oerlikon gunners stuck to our guns. This would mean that all guns would be fully manned at all times of action. George agreed to the idea and some marines were detailed to keep watches with us when we put to sea. The reason we had no merchant seamen gunners was that the fo'c'sle crowd, the greasers and firemen were all lascars who did not, on the whole, make reliable members of a gun's crew.

The gunners had their own mess, a bunk-lined, elongated place with a table running down the centre. It was below decks and the only entrance, and exit, was through a booby-hatch next to number two hold.

The ship itself was of about seven thousand tons. In peace-time she had probably run to Singapore, carrying a score of passengers and a substantial cargo. Now, some of her cargo decks had been cleared and hammock hooks fitted on the beams for troop accommodation. Poor devils, I thought, packed down in the hold like that—not that we should be much better off if the ship was torpedoed. It appeared that there were crash-panels which we could break easily if the booby-hatch doors were jammed or obstructed, but the escape was only onto a troop-deck which would be crammed with soldiers fighting their way out of another narrow exit. My mind was filled with pictures of troops bayoneting one another out of the way in attempts to clear the escape hatches. Two merchant seamen had assured me that this had happened on a ship at St. Nazaire they had both been on. Having something of the behaviour of men under similar conditions I was prepared at least to suspend my disbelief in the story, but it hung about in my mind as I watched the soldiers, sailors, marines and airmen embarking a week later as we lay at anchor off Gourock, and I tried to pick out the faces of those who would panic in an emergency. It was impossible of course, except in one or two obvious cases, but it whiled away an afternoon.

In all we embarked about three hundred men. The Royal Marines and Fleet Air Arm ratings were going out to different places where replacements were needed. The soldiers and airmen were chiefly N.C.O.s of a C3 category who were going to fill stores jobs and to occupy vacant office stools—and no doubt behave like *burra sahibs* after they had been out there for a month. Where "there" was we had no idea beyond the fact that it was somewhere East. Some of the cargo was clearly marked PENANG, but we didn't expect to be going there as it was now in the hands of the Japanese. Still, one never could be certain. Such brass-hat blunders did occur.

George Samson, the Royal Marine corporal and senior gunlayer was a pleasant, fatherly person in his forties. He had a red face and almost completely bald head. With his hooked nose, high cheekbones and erect posture he might have passed as a redskin chief who had run away to sea off a film-set. On the reserve list in 1939, George had been brought back into the Corps just one year after he had settled down to enjoy a peaceful life with his family, following his twenty two years' service in "The Royals." Many R.M. reservists were sent into DEMS both as shore instructors and as sea-going gunlayers at the outbreak of war.

George had a dry, brittle, service humour, used speech economically and talked in a husky voice as though suffering from a perpetual sore throat. Like the rest of us he did not wear uniform on board ship, but pottered about in overalls, or more often, trousers and a homely cardigan. In this rig he always looked as if he had just come in from the garden.

The seaman-gunner who had joined the ship at the same time as George was in appearance unprepossessing, with a dingy complexion and hang-dog demeanour. His uniform was sloppy and food-stained, his hair matted. He was about thirty, an orphan and unmarried; his only next-of-kin was a distant aunt whom he had not seen since the beginning of the war. He never took any of his leaves because he said he had nowhere to go, so he always stayed aboard the ship, going ashore for necessities and to the pictures occasionally, always alone. He seemed a repulsively dull character to me, and I could never understand George's attachment to him, for he seemed to see only the good points in Ralph—as the gunner was called—whereas I, and the others, saw only the bad.

The other two seamen-gunners were sprogs of eighteen who had been pressed into the DEMS service after being called up for the Royal Navy. One was a green boy from Stoke-on-Trent, the other a miner's son from the Welsh valleys. Both fell out of their bunks in the Clyde while the ship was at anchor and we ragged them mercilessly about this, but Ralph showed them how to make their bunks properly so that they wouldn't fall out of them. He hadn't taken part in the ragging.

Teddy Fox, one of the gunlayers, was a quiet, intelligent man who had been the assistant editor of a well-known literary weekly, while his friend, Tom Potter, was a prep. schoolmaster "in real life," as he put it. The other gunlayer, John Griffiths, was an ex-farmer, profoundly Welsh, organ voiced and chain smoking.

These then were my immediate sailing companions. We would sleep and eat together for heaven knew how long. There would be little mixing with the merchant seamen, as on our other ships, owing to the fact that the crew were mainly lascars who had their own quarters and galley, besides their own cook. Hideous smells issued from the lascar galley aft as the chef and his assistant prepared and cooked the dried fish which they kept stored in large baskets and which, together with ghee, an Indian clarified butter, seemed to form the coloured men's main diet. Occasionally they would bring the fish up on deck and air it, hanging it on lines like washing, then taking it down at night and stowing it away somewhere below.

The only one of the lascars who could converse in fluent English was Akbar, the serang, or bos'n. He was a small, lithe man of indeterminate age but certainly not young. He smiled often but not obsequiously as the others did. Whereas most of the lascars were resigned, passive and on the whole melancholy, Akbar was vital and efficient, neither fawning on those above him, nor bullying to those beneath him. He was a first-rate seaman and respected by everybody who came into contact with him.

The ship's officers were of course whites. They seemed more habitually aloof than other M.N. officers I'd met, possibly through always sailing with native crews. It had made them draw together, and stand apart, more. When, for instance, a young radio officer had become friendly with one of the younger gunners about his own age and with obviously similar tastes, the sparks was reprimanded for mixing with naval ratings and reminded that he was primarily an officer. Primarily he was a young man of course, and the only young whites in the ship's company were the seaman-gunners, apart from two cadets who would have nothing to do with him. However, he was forbidden the gunners' company and our quarters were put out of bounds to him.

II

IT WAS snowing hard when we sailed from the Clyde in the company of several other ships bound in a southerly direction.

We sailed along the coast of Northern Ireland in a comparatively carefree manner, knowing that there were few U-boats in that area. Now that the United States were in the war the Germans were concentrating on the American eastern seaboard and the Caribbean, the first sinkings taking place on January 12th, 1942. The enemy were of course trying to stop the flow of oil from Aruba, Curaçao, the Gulfs of Venezuela and of Mexico. Dozens of tankers were in the habit of sailing peacefully and independently up from the Gulfs to join convoys en route for the U.K. Besides these the Germans found easy pickings in the innumerable coastal vessels which plied between the Panama area and the eastern U.S. seaports. The U-boats concentrated most of these anti-American attacks on such areas as Hampton Roads, North Carolina and Cape Hatteras, and from the 12th to the end of January they sank thirty-nine ships, sixteen of which were tankers, the whole totalling nearly a quarter of a million tons. When torpedoes ran out the submarines often surfaced and used their guns on the unescorted vessels. One U-boat prisoner later described it as a U-boat's paradise.

We did not know about all these sinkings when we were setting out on this trip. All we knew was that the Germans were not concentrating U-boats off the coast of Northern Ireland, as they had done in earlier phases of the Battle of the Atlantic, and this knowledge alone made us feel easier, but strict watches were kept all the same.

As we steamed southwards the weather grew warmer and we began to shed duffel coats and jerseys. The gunners kept watch and watch in these waters, that is to say, four hours on and four off. I had the starboard side bridge Oerlikon. The turret was not exactly on the bridge but just abaft it, and had to be entered by means of a short ladder from the bridge wing. Each Oerlikon gunner had a Royal Marine as his number two, or loading number. The drums of ammunition for these guns, each containing sixty rounds and weighing about forty pounds, needed skilful handling. They had to be swung to a height above the gun, then dropped neatly into position so that they locked themselves over the breech, all in one movement.

These 20 mm. guns were superbly accurate and a delight to shoot. The gunner stepped into two curved and rubber-cushioned shoulder pieces, then passed a broad leather strap round his waist and clipped it to the other side of the gun. He could then lie back and shoot at any angle necessary, even a vertical one. There was very little recoil or vibration, this being absorbed by the huge steel springs round the barrel. We usually loaded one tracer in every four rounds of ammunition, the rest being H.E. shells, though there were other varieties for use such as armour-piercing and shrapnel.

We soon changed into tropical kit, though the gunners' was very informal. Mine usually consisted of khaki shorts and gym shoes during the day time, with a shirt, a chequered Australian lumberjacket and a lifejacket added at night. On the inside of my lifejacket I had stitched a canvas bag. In this bag was a sealed, flat-fifty type of cigarette tin; in the tin was my paybook and one English pound note. I had obeyed the orders of the DEMS paymaster in Glasgow to the letter. Moreover, I had enough money to pay for a survivor's bus ride and to buy shaving tackle. I might even have enough money left to buy myself some overalls. I certainly did not intend to wander again over half some country until the Navy provided me with the few necessaries of a matelot's life. I also carried a long sheath-knife at my belt, convinced that this would be useful in almost any emergency.

The Marine who shared my watch was a silent, inscrutable fellow. Pink and scrubbed in appearance, he would stand for practically the entire four hours staring at the same spot on the horizon, as if he were in a sentry box. About half-way through the watch he would ask if he could go and get the "kye." This was cocoa issued to watch-keepers and was so thick that after drinking it one felt silted up inside. Marine Wright would become comparatively matey as we gobbled—for one can hardly say "drank"—the hot mud, and he once went so far conversationally as to tell me he had a dog at home named Sam. But after such a flight of loquacity he would set down his mug and stiffen towards the horizon for another two hours.

Topees issued to naval ratings must be the most cumbersome pieces of headgear ever worn. As big as beehives, these solar hats are usually only worn to order. On my first voyage to tropical countries I had tried to master the art of wearing one but had failed utterly. When I bent my head forwards it fell off. It fell off when I leaned backwards, and even if it were worn with the chinstrap in position one was either mildly throttled by it, or else it swung round to the front and hung like a begging-bowl or a horse's nosebag. Consequently I gave up trying to wear a topee and went in for piratical headpieces when the weather was very hot. These consisted of simply the nearest piece of material to hand, such as a towel or handkerchief, to be worn wrapped round the head and draped over the nape of the neck.

It was not until I joined the *Astrid* that the true art of wearing a naval topee was made apparent to me. When I was on watch one day, Marine Wright being as usual in what seemed to be a catatonic trance, I turned for visual relaxation to look at the figures on the bridge. One of them, a naval signalman, I had not seen before and concluded that he must only recently have been detailed to keep a bridge lookout. I had seen some strange sights at sea, even in my short experience, but I had never before seen a monocled matelot. I had previously heard that there was a sailor among the Fleet Air Arm ratings who sported a monocle, but I thought it was just a yarn, like the one about the golden rivet. Yet here he was, a man of about thirty-five, with a gaunt, faintly aristocratic appearance—even without his monocle—dressed in tropical shirt and shorts both three sizes too big for him and, this is the point, *sheltering* under an outsize naval topee. So *that* was how to wear one! You simply had to shelter under it.

Ordinary Signalman Pauncefort-Dundas was an Old Etonian with gentle manners and an alert mind. He had broken loose from some Ministry job only a few months earlier, had pulled strings to get himself into the Navy, and had Admiralty permission to wear his monocle. This permission was, I believe, granted to only two men in the Royal Navy during the war. Ordinary Signalman Pauncefort-Dundas was one of them. Being highly literate he had been given a pen-pusher's or scribe's job in an office ashore after completing his naval training—not that this called for high literacy—but Pauncefort-Dundas had not gone to a lot of trouble to join the Navy in order to do minor clerical work. He was not A1 because of his defective eye, so he could not be appointed to a ship, but he could volunteer for a foreign shore signal-station draft, and this is what he had done. So now he was watchkeeping his passage on the *Astrid,* working his way East. We got on extremely well, and I asked him how he came to be able to wear a naval pith-helmet without practice.

"I wore a bowler for a long time, you know," he reminded me.

I told him that many M.N. captains wore bowlers at sea, favouring the narrow-brimmed hat which did not easily blow off. He told me that he knew a girl who once went to a party wearing a live mouse in her hair. It was tethered by one hind leg to a hairpin. *It* did not easily blow off.

III

WE FIRST met trouble off Cape Verde Islands. This was presaged by a disturbing incident as we approached the islands. Our convoy consisted of some twenty-odd ships including several troopers and an escort of seven destroyers. We sailed at fifteen knots most of the time, this being a fast convoy. The *Astrid's* station was 1.4. Therefore she was the fourth ship in the port flank. One afternoon we sighted what seemed to be a fishing boat with a dark red sail.

"Out from St. Vincent I expect," commented Captain Wilson, lowering his binoculars. "We're not more than twenty miles off there."

Everyone on the bridge muttered respectfully and turned to other things. The captain was a man to command respect : tall, dignified, laconic, but what was most important, a great seaman. He knew his saltwater world, though in this particular instance his judgment was at fault. Ordinary Signalman Pauncefort-Dundas had not taken his eyes off the "fishing boat." He continued to stare at it after it had dropped astern of the convoy, the late afternoon sun glinting on his monocle.

"Captain, sir," he said suddenly.

"What is it, Signalman?"

"That boat, sir. Her sail is on fire," Pauncefort-Dundas reported calmly.

"What?"

Captain Wilson spun round. Half a dozen pairs of binoculars and a telescope were focussed on the small vessel. It was true enough : the dark red sail had changed to bright orange and was being consumed by fire even as we watched. A long, lean destroyer raced towards the boat from the stern of the convoy.

A few hours later we received the news that the craft was a ship's boat which had been adrift for nearly a month. In it were the bodies of six men. The seventh was just alive, too weak to tip the bodies of his dead companions "over the wall" as they had succumbed, one after the other, to death by thirst and exposure. He was just able to dash some paraffin from a hurricane lamp onto the sail and put a match to it when he realized that the first ships he had sighted were ignoring him. This lone survivor was now safe in the destroyer's sick bay, no doubt being well looked after, but in my mind I could see his bloated tongue, the boat-sores which covered his thin body, his prematurely grey hair, long, matted, and his yellow, staring eyes.

The report made us all stir our tea thoughtfully as the sun went swiftly down. That night we ran into heavy weather and the ship began to roll mightily. I came up to take the middle at five minutes to twelve and was just climbing the starboard bridge ladder when I saw on the port beam what seemed like the effect of a violent explosion. It looked like an ammo ship blowing up, but there was no sound above the roar of the wind and waters. Immediately I called the attention of the third mate who was still on the bridge with the captain, both of them in long dripping oilskins. The third's big, moonlike face grinned at me.

"That's ball lightning, laddie," he shouted, "and look, there on the masthead, Elmo's Fire!"

He pointed to the foremast top where the ghostly blue-green phosphorescence was beginning to form both there and on the spars. I had never seen the electrical phenomenon before, though I had heard and read about it. I stared in wonder at the strange sight, feeling as though I ought to cross myself, though I'm not a Catholic.

"Have you no been in these waters before?" the third mate bawled in my ear.

"Yes, but I've never been in such an electric storm," I shouted back.

"It's one of the best," the third said through the veil of rain which streamed off his sou'-wester.

I climbed into my turret and was joined a few minutes later by Marine Wright. We were not relieving anyone in this turret, the earlier starboard Oerlikon watch having been kept on the boat-deck gun. We were doing four on and eight hours off in these comparatively safe waters. Teddy Fox was now in the port boat-deck turret with his number two, and only one of the seaman-gunners was aft on the 4-inch gun platform. The rest were happily asleep in their bunks.

The watch passed quickly as there was plenty to see, with ball lightning bursting on the horizon and fork lightning rending the heavens, not to mention the excitement of seeing other ships loom at us through the darkness then sheer away as their lookouts spotted us and shouted warnings to their bridges. We too nearly ran into the stern of the ship ahead of us. It became impossible to keep station so the commodore signalled all ships to sail in open order and use navigation lights until the worst of the storm was over.

I went off watch at four in the morning with some misgivings. The wind was higher if anything, though there was no electrical warfare and as it had stopped raining visibility had improved and navigation lights had been turned off. Usually I found it difficult to sleep during storms at sea and always preferred to watch them on deck, but to-night I felt cold an stiff so I went below. Teddy had brought some cocoa down to the mess so we sat at the table drinking it and quietly discussing pornography in English literature, a favourite topic of conversation between Teddy and myself. We tried to arrive at a true definition of pornography—in a tired sort of way—and were arguing about the American judge's famous decisions regarding the publication of *Ulysses*, when a fearful rumbling began in the bowels of the ship.

Each rumble ended in a terrifying crash as the ship rolled to port or starboard. Sounds of shouting and movement came from the troop-deck. The men were awake, not that many of them had been asleep in this weather, and were clamouring to get on deck. All the gunners woke up and scrambled out of their bunks into lifejackets and seaboots.

"What's in number two hold?" I asked George who was instantly alert on waking, the old campaigner.

"Those boom-defence sinkers," he said.

"God!" I gasped.

The *Astrid* carried a lot of boom-defence gear and I remembered seeing the seven-ton pyramidal concrete sinkers being lowered into the hold next to our quarters when the ship was in Glasgow. One, or some of them, had been badly stowed and were sliding about on top of the others, crashing into the bulkheads as we rolled. I was reminded of a film I'd seen before the war in which a steam roller, carried as part of the deck cargo of a China-bound trampship, broke loose in a storm and careered about the deck, crushing coolies by the dozen. I was just worrying whether Clark Gable was the hero of the film or not, when another rumble started as we rolled to port. This was followed by a resounding crash, the loudest of them all. My mind froze.

"Another like that and it'll be through the side," said Tom Potter, anxiously.

"Let's get on deck, then!" shouted John Griffiths round a newly-lighted cigarette.

It seemed a sensible idea. We collected oilskins and hurried up the ladder, out through the booby hatchway. The third mate's big face greeted us.

"Just the boys I wanted. Follow me," he said, as if we had volunteered for something.

We followed him down into the stores where, he said, there was a watertight door which opened onto number two hold. We reached it and Three Mates pulled back the steel fastenings then swung the door open. Crowding round, we peered into the blackness. Nothing, at first, then as the ship began to roll to starboard and a loud rumbling began on the port side, the third flashed his torch. We saw two of the huge concrete sinkers starting their journey across the hold to the opposite bulkhead, sliding over the big ringbolts which protruded from the tops of the sinkers stowed below.

"Christ!" breathed George, down my neck.

"Quick, inside," ordered the third mate. "There are some big timbers lying about. We must get them and ram 'em down between the blocks below as soon as the loose sinkers ride back to this side. They'll act as wedges and stop the blocks from sliding back."

We stepped inside the hold and began to climb across the sinkers, the tops of which measured about four feet by four, with the ringbolts in the middle. There was a lot of timber between them and we collected some of the larger pieces as we moved carefully accross the hold. Someone else had arrived with lamps and we could see better now, but the rumbling went on, loud and ominous, as the two blocks neared the starboard bulkhead. Crash! Crash! The pair of them hit it almost together and we expected water to spurt through the broken plates, but somehow they held. The blocks began to travel back to port as the vessel, after steadying onto an even keel for a few seconds, began to roll to that side. I jumped from the top of the sinker on which I had been standing to the top of the one next to it, about five feet away. I did this in order to get a large batten I'd spotted lying between this block and the one on the other side of it. I was trying to haul it out when my foot slipped and down I crashed between the blocks.

"Stay where you are and keep your head down!" the third mate yelled as he saw me trying to claw my way up the face of one of the pyramids.

I did as I was bid, listening in a sweat of terror to the loose blocks rumbling towards me as I flattened myself against the one I'd slipped from. If all went well the sinkers would ride harmlessly over my head, sliding over the ringbolts. If not. . . . I cursed myself and tried to hold my breath. The blocks roared and scraped overhead, blotting out the light from the torches and lanterns and showering me with concrete dust and chippings. Then I could see the lights again and the blocks smashed into the bulkhead, sickeningly.

"Now!" yelled the third.

The men were flinging timbers, all they could lay hands on, into the pit next to the loose blocks, the biggest on end to serve as wedges. I scrambled out from my funkhole with my piece of wood and joined in the timber-slinging party. As the ship rolled to starboard the blocks this time remained fixed, jammed up against the port bulkhead by our timbers. One of the seamen-gunners cheered.

"Not finished yet," said the Third. "Let's put some more in to make sure."

We got some more old railway sleepers and rammed them into position then passed some mooring ropes which the serang had produced through the ringbolts of the runaway blocks, and secured them to the ringbolts of the blocks below. There would be seven tons too much on one side of the ship, but the third assured us that this was nothing to worry about and could be evened up elsewhere. There would have to be quite a lot of cargo re-trimming done when we got to Freetown in a few days' time. Captain Wilson, who had come down to see if all was well, thanked us for our help and gave George a bottle of whisky for the gunners' mess. We went back to enjoy it.

IV

FOUR DAYS later we dropped anchor inside the bar at Freetown, Sierra Leone. It was an exciting moment for many on board who had never before visited a foreign country or smelt the coast of Africa. Twice I had previously been in this harbour but never set foot on the land, and I had come to regard this dark green humpish African coast with awe. For me this *was* Africa with its exotic smells of mangoes, oranges, citrons, inextricably mixed with what I fancied to be lion, though it might well have been man. Here was the real, dark green mystery I had read about in Conrad's *Heart of Darkness,* just beyond the jungle fringe I could see from the ship. I had been to Cape Town and Durban but they were tame, Euro-Americanized; places where you bought nylon stockings to take home, went to the cinema, parties, dances, drove about in big, purring cars, were taken to the races. They were not Africa: here, the West Coast, this was Africa. In a way I hoped I should never have to go ashore and spoil the illusion.

We lay at anchor for five days, the bumboats swarming round us like water-flies, except for the two or three occasions when we lowered our boats for drill purposes. This included both boat pulling and sailing and was welcomed as a diversion by most of the men on board, especially those soldiers and airmen who had never been in small boats before, though not the ones who were violently sick. We swam in large numbers—a precaution against sharks which abound in the bay but which keep clear of commotion in the water, unless they smell blood. All the gunners except Ralph bathed daily. He apparently couldn't swim and watched us with envy as we dived from the after well-deck or the waist and climbed back up the scramble-nets which had been let down the ship's sides for that purpose. I felt fit and wonderfully happy, until the day we sailed when something else occurred to remind us of the horror which sometimes lies just beneath the surface of the beauty of life. Superstition grows on those who go to sea, occasioned partly by experiences and associations, often personal ones. Few of the old superstitions, such as sailing on a Friday, exist to-day even among the most ancient, shellbacked, fo'c'sle men. These tales are kept alive only by the artificial respiration of lubberly writers. It is in incidents such as the following that sailors see their fate.

Most of the bumboat men who flog their wares of fruit, and baskets made of cane and coloured raffia, are young musclemen, good swimmers, strong paddlers who can shovel their slim craft swiftly along even against the nine knot tide of this bay. But there was one old ragged grandad of a man who came out every day to the ship and had become a favourite with the troops to whom he sold good fruit without overcharging : pineapples at fourpence apiece, mangoes threepence a dozen. He was alongside saying his Goodbye-God-Bless-King-George on our last afternoon. The anchors were weighed and we were just awaiting the return of the ship's launch with some last-minute stores before clearing the bar and getting into our convoy station. The old bumboat man was packing his wares preparatory to paddling clear of the ship when the launch appeared, making a wide arc round the stern to this, the port side, where it was to be hoisted in. The coxswain put the tiller hard over to come alongside, or rather he *tried* to put the tiller hard over. But either it or the rudder had jammed and the heavy launch came straight on at the old negro's boat. With a yell he tried to fling himself out of the way, but he was too old and feeble to make much of an attempt. The stempiece of the launch carved his boat in two and crushed him against the ship's side, breaking his head open like an egg. The coxswain was so busy shoving the gears into the astern position to check the launch's speed when he found the tiller jammed, that he hardly knew what had happened until he was flung face downward into the bottom of his boat. We on deck couldn't reach down to help the old man who was by now beyond assistance. His blood and brains were spattered on the ship's side, the bumboat was mere flotsam with a few mangoes and a raffia basket floating pathetically in the water near it, while already the sharks were tearing the old man's body, turning and tearing with their hideous mouths.

The launch was hoisted inboard and the ship's propellers began to turn. One turn of the screw pays all debts, the sailor says. The incident would be reported to the shore authorities by radio, of course, but meanwhile the war must go on. Unfortunately the troops saw the accident in terms of White v. Black—people *have* to be on a side—especially when the coxswain, one of the junior engineers, was crass enough to remark as soon as he came on board :

"Serve the black bastard right. He shouldn't have been in the way."

I doubt very much if he meant this, but suspect that he was considerably shocked himself and tried not to show it by using tough talk to hide his feelings. However, words sometimes have a way of seeming to mean just what they say, so the engineer nearly got himself dumped over the side by a group of soldiers who heard the remark. They were stopped by one of their own officers, while the flustered and foolish engineer hurried off to his quarters in some midships penetralia.

I went up to the starboard turret to take The Dogs, the four to eight watch, with Marine Wright. For four hours we stood in silence, watching the African coast grow darker and smaller until finally, after the sun had made its rapid, equatorial descent we could see it no longer. The night sea-wind suddenly blew cold, and with the cold and the darkness came fear, a fear I recognized but did not understand, then.

V

It was near the Ides of March and the Soothsayer had cried out, Beware. But although it was almost the anniversary of the action I had been in hundreds of miles farther north the previous year, I was not particularly nervous after the night we left Freetown. It was ridiculous, I told myself. It couldn't happen again on the same date to the same person, even in another part of the ocean. Besides, we were in safe waters now. In a day or two we should be leaving the convoy, or they would be leaving us, as we were the slowest of the half-dozen ships now steaming south. Proof enough, and if further proof were needed we hadn't even got an escort, not one destroyer, corvette or frigate. All the U-boats, it was now said, were in the Caribbean, or up off the U.S. eastern seaboard having a whale of a time. There was no need to worry.

As we neared the equator the troops found it impossibly stuffy on their mess-decks, and most of them slept on the hatches and cargo decks. We used to fall over them as they sprawled on the iron decks with only one blanket underneath and one over the top of them. How they envied us our comparative privacy and mattressed bunks! Some of the soldiers never got the knack of sleeping in slung hammocks. They finally gave up trying and just dossed among their kit in any quiet corner they could find. Occasionally we took a couple of marines, soldiers, or R.A.F. men down to our mess and gave them a decent meal. Our food was no better than theirs, but there was more of it and it looked better on plates than in mess-traps.

Ordinary Signalman Pauncefort-Dundas had amused himself and many of those on board during the past two weeks by editing a ship's magazine entitled, ASTRID. Teddy Fox was the assistant editor. They had managed to get hold of a typewriter and duplicating machine from somewhere on the ship and had produced fifty copies of the first issue of the magazine. These were passed round the ship and read by nearly every man who could read. ASTRID contained stories, articles, day-by-day news officially released from the bridge, jokes and a crossword which no one but a classics don could have completed. One day I discovered Pauncefort-Dundas compiling one of these monstrosities with the aid of a battered, dog-eared Lemprière which he apparently always carried in his kit. He looked up.

"You didn't have a public school education, did you?" he asked.

"No," I answered, hoping he wasn't going to ask me the name of the tribe of frenzied women who tore Orpheus apart, or some other thing I couldn't remember.

"Pity," sighed Pauncefort-Dundas. "They often turn out some very good ex-rugger players."

"I'll remember that next time I'm thinking of my children's future," I said.

Preparations were made for a Crossing-The-Line ceremony as we pressed southwards. I had had my ducking months before and considered myself an initiate, a denizen of Neptune's Deeps. Rude and personal remarks were directed at Ralph who, it was said, would get his first good wash of the voyage when Neptune's coppers caught him.

March 16th, the exact anniversary date of the *Vesta's* sinking, passed uneventfully and the next day George, for some reason I never understood or even tried to, reshuffled the watches so that I now had the eight to twelve instead of The Dogs. This meant that I had twelve hours off on March 17th and it suited me well. I slept from nine in the morning until late in the afternoon and when I awoke it was like being reborn. After tea I still had three clear hours before I went on watch again with Marine Wright, so I decided to write a few letters, or at least start a letter to Daria in Baltimore, in the hope of producing a really substantial epistle which I could post in about ten days' time at Cape Town, our next port of call. I was never a great letter writer and the only way I could ever pen a detailed one was by using the diary form. So I put my name on a sheet of paper and began to write. I couldn't give the name of the ship as I intended to post the letter

ashore in Cape Town and the postmark might have betrayed the
ship's whereabouts. This information might have been conveyed
to Germany by some extremely roundabout method in perhaps a
year or two's time, thus arriving as historical war-data or late
evidence in support of some agent's claim to have seen the ship—
perhaps even worked on it—while posing as a Capetown docker.
One couldn't be too careful.

I struggled to think of things to say concerning myself and my
travels after the usual preliminary inquiries about Daria's relations and herself. I didn't find it easy, in view of possible censor-
ship, so I gave up and tried to write about the things I was seeing
around me, the flying fish and Portuguese men-o'-war. But then
I reflected that this might give an indication that the ship was
in tropical seas, and the censor would probably cut it out, so there
was no point in writing it. I put the paper and pen away and
went on deck.

Akbar, the serang, greeted me with an informal salute.

"Ship sail all alone now, Gunner-Sahib. We in fairly safe
waters," he smiled.

I looked round and saw no ships.

"When did they leave us, Akbar?"

"At seven bells this forenoon, Sahib. You were watch-below
then? You sleep deep?"

"About six fathoms."

"Sahib? Oh, yes, I understand. I sleep like that when I am
young man. Now have only one fathom sleeps, like this."

He pressed the pale palms of his hands together and rested his
cheek against them in a forty winks attitude, then he turned and
went off to the lascars' galley.

"Good old Akbar," a husky voice said.

George sidled up to me smoking his pipe, feet shuffling along
the iron deck in sandals. We both leaned on the ship's rail and
stared out to sea.

"All right now aren't we, George? Next stop District 15?" I
said heartily.

District 15 was a dock area of Cape Town famed for prostitu-
tion and knifings in the back. It was out of bounds to all British
servicemen.

"I suppose so," George wheezed, without much enthusiasm,
as if he would rather be at home, putting in a row of beans.

He changed the subject.

"Should cross the Line about midnight. Celebrations to-morrow
—all being well."

"All being well? Don't be such an old pessimist, George," I
remonstrated. "By the way, are you one of Neptune's coppers?"

"How d'you know I ain't the old bastard himself?" George muttered round his pipe.

He took it from his mouth but a thread of drool hung from his lower lip to the stem, still linking him to it. He noticed the spit-thread and jabbed the pipe back in his mouth as if ashamed. He smoothed and patted his shiny sunburnt dome.

"Ah well, head down for half an hour. Got the eight to twelve with old Ralph," he said.

"How ghastly for you," I sympathized.

"Oh, he's all right, is Ralph," George answered.

He turned and headed for the booby-hatch down to our mess. I lingered by the rail for half an hour or so, idly watching our progress through the golden waters, past the lifting, silver, flying fish.

At five minutes to eight I climbed the starboard bridge ladder up to my gun and three minutes later Marine Wright appeared beside me in the turret. We nodded to each other but did not speak. He took up his usual sentry-go position while I swept the horizon with my binoculars. John Griffiths was in the after turret, port side, doing the same thing, fag in mouth as usual. It would be his last smoke on deck this watch, for although smoking was allowed in daylight hours to relieve the tedium of watchkeeping, it was now dusk and when darkness fell a cigarette glow could be seen a mile away by the naked eye, and at a much greater distance with binoculars, so of course it was forbidden then.

At half past eight Marine Wright went for cocoa and sandwiches. When he returned we sat and munched the hunks of bully-beef and bread, then attempted to swallow some of the kye, just as our part of the earth turned its back on the sun and plunged itself into darkness. It blew cold. I put on my lumber-jacket and lifejacket on top of that for warmth. Marine Wright shrugged himself into a service greatcoat he had brought on watch with him. On the bridge I could see the figures of the captain, the third mate, who was officer-of-the-watch, and the quartermaster just inside the wheelhouse. By standing on the top step inside the turret I could see down to the fo'c'sle and the hatch of number one hold. About twenty R.A.F. men were in the habit of sleeping on top of this hatch every night. I could see them now, some unrolling blankets, others already kipped down. It seemed a good spot for sleeping, away from the engine noise, smell and vibration. On the other side of the bridge the troops who were not on the mess-deck playing cards or reading were bedding down beside and on top of number two hatch. Someone was playing a mouth-organ half under his blanket. It was a plaintive sound, a faint, muted agony expressing perhaps the player's homesickness, or his sadness of life generally.

The moon was out, the silver sea calm and peaceful. I looked at the time by my watch: nine o'clock on a fine clear night and all was well.

BANG!

The ship seemed to leap out of the sea and her bows explode as the torpedo struck just below number one hold, forward of of the bridge. A huge column of water soared into the air, then came crashing down onto the decks and bridge, filling the gun turret. As the ship steadied herself and started to settle down at the head I stood up on the top step inside the turret, rubbed the smarting salt water out of my eyes and peered over the bridge at the damage. The hatch had been blown open and I could see the moon reflected in the water which had already filled the hold. I looked up at the mast. There, blown up into the rigging, draped, entangled and hanging from it, were the bodies and parts of bodies of some of the men who had been asleep on the hatch. The rest, I supposed, had been blown over the side.

The siren began to blow, loud, insistent, hideous. Six blasts, three times. ABANDON SHIP, ABANDON SHIP, ABANDON SHIP. We were sinking fast. I turned to Marine Wright and found him lying half out of the other side of the turret, headless. I remembered that he had been standing upright as usual when the torpedo struck us. Some flying metal fragment must have hit him, axed off his head like a bloody executioner. All I could think of at the time was, I wonder if Sam will miss him?

I wanted to do something, anything, shoot the gun for instance. I lashed the harness round myself, took out the stop-pin and trained the Oerlikon back and forth to see if it were free. A calm voice said:

"No point in doing that, old man. Go to your boat station."

It was the captain. He was standing near the top of the bridge ladder, watching the boats being cleared and lowered into the sea. His voice sounded heavy and sad. I unlashed the harness and climbed out of the turret, dripping wet.

"I'm in your boat, sir," I said.

"Tell them not to wait," he answered.

"But sir——" I protested.

"I'll be all right," he replied, then pointed to a Carley float lashed to the side of the wheelhouse. "There's always that."

"We'll look out for you then, sir," I said.

He seemed to smile grimly as I passed him.

"Good luck," he said.

I hurried down the ladder and slipped on a patch of oil at the bottom, cursed and scrabbled on the sloping iron deck for something to clutch at, found a ringbolt and hauled myself up. The ship was listing to starboard but not heavily and all the boats had been lowered, including the two on the port side. This operation had been accomplished under the direction of the third mate, who had then gone to the saloon to get himself a glass of whisky, after which he had taken one up to the captain on the bridge. This must surely have been the most courteous act in the whole history of whisky drinking.

My boat was number two, starboard side. They were just shoving off when I arrived, but waited while I climbed down the scramble net and jumped into the boat. We started to pull away from the ship with the boat heavily overcrowded. Suddenly someone shouted :

"There's somebody still on deck !"

I looked up and saw a figure heaving hatchboards over the rail. These were two-inch thick boards, about five feet long and two feet wide and were used to cover the cargo hatches before a large canvas sheet was spread over them. It was Ralph who was throwing the boards over, staggering backwards and forwards under the weight of them. I recognized him by the dirty white wool cap he always wore.

"Ralph !" I shouted. "Jump for it, man. We'll pick you up !"

For an answer he just turned and waved his arm, then went to get another hatchboard. The boat drew away from the ship a hundred, two hundred yards. We stopped to pluck a lascar from a hatchboard he had been lying on face downwards and canoeing with his hands. There was a curious underwater fizzing noise near the boat and another explosion as the second torpedo struck the *Astrid* right under number three hold, the one from which Ralph had been collecting hatchboards. In a few minutes the stern of the vessel reared high out of the water and vertically she plunged hissing and booming, under the waves.

Silence.

Then, borne on the night wind, came the faint, plaintive music of the mouth-organ, its owner bobbing on a raft some distance away. Soon we could hear soldiers' voices singing the chorus :

> *I belong to Glasgow,*
> *Dear Old Glasgow Town. . . .*

and somebody handed cigarettes round the boat.

"Submarine surfacing, sir," one of the apprentices said rapidly to the second officer who was in charge of the boat.

"Any Service officers here?" the second asked anxiously.

"Yes," answered a voice, "Squadron Leader Mansfield."

"Please remove your badges of rank, sir," the second mate urged.

"Are you trying to be funny? I'm in my pyjamas."

Laughter in the boat, until the second hissed:

"Be quiet! They may not have spotted us. Everybody down in the boat."

We lay and crouched as low as possible, but there were too many of us to get flat and we bulged over the gunwales.

"Really, gentlemen, it is no use trying to hide," a cold voice spoke out of the blue, a few minutes later.

We sat upright, all feeling slightly ridiculous, and found we were practically tied up alongside the U-boat. It was a large, cruising type with an 88 mm. gun mounted on the fore-casing. A few sailors in white shorts and jerseys stood on the casing, eyeing us. Two of them had sub-machine guns, one a rifle, but they did not point them at us. In the conning tower high above us the U-boat commander stood, without doubt master of the situation and very conscious of it. I could not see his face clearly, but he seemed to have a beard and wore a white-topped cap and muffler. His English was excellent.

"Is there an officer in the boat?" he asked, no longer mocking.

"I am the second officer," replied that gentleman.

"Ah, good. Your ship was the motor vessel *Astrid,* was she not?" the German questioned rhetorically.

No answer.

"Where was she bound?"

"I wasn't told her ultimate destination," the second mate answered sullenly.

"I see. You were probably to receive orders at Cape Town. What was your cargo?"

The second mate was silent for a minute, then he answered quickly:

"General."

"And how many crew?"

The soldiers on the raft were singing again. Perhaps the German didn't know we carried troops? Fearfully we wondered.

"Seventy four," the second answered truthfully, as this was the number of the crew, including the gunners.

The U-boat commander seemed to be listening intently to the singing. Presently he asked:

"They are Scottish men?"

"Half a dozen of them are," the quick-witted mate replied.

"They have good hearts," the commander said.

I hoped he wouldn't cruise round and see the troops. They would quite likely be machine-gunned even by this courteous German. Merchant seamen were of civilian status, but soldiers, Royal Marines, naval ratings and R.A.F. men came under another heading. It was unlikely that the German would spare them to possibly fight another day.

"What happened to your captain?" the commander asked suddenly.

"Went down with the ship," answered the second.

"How traditional," said the German. "I am very sorry to hear that. I am also very sorry to have caused you this inconvenience by sinking your ship, but in the classic phrase, war is war. I am also sorry not to be able to spare you any supplies, as we are short ourselves. Incidentally, are there any ship's gunners in your boat?"

I wondered if it would be possible to go over the side of the boat without being observed. There was no need.

"No," replied the second mate, "we think they went down with the ship, too."

There was a pause while the commander appeared to consult somebody in the control room below the conning tower, then he said:

"I understand. Well, gentlemen, your position is approximately 32 minutes north, 18° west. If you were near land I would tow you to the shore, but alas, it is three hundred miles to Liberia, which is the nearest coast from here, and I cannot spare the time, nor the risk to my boat. I do not like to desert you, but. . . ."

He shrugged hugely.

"There is no alternative."

He gave curt, German orders to the sailors who nimbly climbed the conning tower ladders and disappeared. The motors started and as the boat swung away from us we noticed that besides the boat's number on the conning tower there was also an insignia: The Ace of Spades.

"Quite a fictional touch," commented the squadron leader, shivering in his pyjamas.

"*Auf Wiedersehen,*" the commander called back out of the darkness. "Good night."

One or two men in the boat answered him.

"Decent bastard," said someone. "Not like most of 'em."

The U-boat had disappeared northwards, away from the other boats and rafts full of troops. The second officer's bluff had worked!

"He didn't know *all* about it anyway," grinned the second. "Now boys, we'll go about and see if we can rope the rafts up."

We pulled about in the moonlit waters, hauling men off hatchboards, taking identity discs and any papers off dead men, drowned men, floating face downwards in Mae Wests they had put on wrongly. Others had obviously jumped over the side wearing the older type of cork lifejacket which, if not held or tied down tightly at the front, knocks the wearer unconscious as soon as he hits the water. Then, of course, unless he is hauled out at once he drowns. Some, we guessed, had died this way. By the time we had picked up odd swimmers and hatchboard paddlers our boat was loaded down to the wash-strake, that is, just below the gunwale. We began to ship water over the gunwales and those in the bottom of the boat, led by Akbar, baled with boots, hands, tins, balers, for all they were worth. Akbar was magnificent. He baled continuously for seven or eight hours, like a machine.

The rafts were roped onto the boats instead of to each other. We kept the boats together and hove to, bows into the wind which had sprung up. We spent the night baling, cursing, and praying, according to inclination. Some did all three to be on the safe side.

To our great joy we found that the captain and third officer were safe and in one of the boats, after having had a miraculous escape. When they had drunk their whiskies on the bridge they unlashed the Carley float and dropped it over the port side. They were knocked flat aback when the second torpedo tore into the *Astrid*, but they got up unhurt and jumped from the bridge into the sea. They struck out for the float, caught hold of the grablines and held on. They were sucked a little way down as the ship sank, but they held their breaths and soon bobbed to the surface and climbed onto the float to be picked up half an hour later by one of the boats.

One thing they had noticed of importance was that as the *Astrid* disappeared under the surface a number of large boom defence floats had burst out of one of the holds and breached like big fishes. They were now floating about in the ocean near at hand, and as soon as it was light the boats would have to round them up. They would be invaluable as extra rafts to take some of the load off the boats. The floats were about twelve feet long, six wide and six deep, made of thick sheet-iron, absolutely watertight. It was a miracle, everybody said, that they had broken loose and surfaced.

A miracle? I wondered. The floats had been in number three hold, the one from which Ralph had ripped back the canvas and heaved hatchboards over the side. Did he know that he would be helping to release the floats when the ship sank, besides more obviously providing temporary hatchboard rafts for those in the water? I vaguely remembered a short conversation I'd had with him—one of the few, alas, I ever had with him—in which we'd discussed the seaworthy appearance of the boom-defence floats and their possible use as rafts in an emergency. Without loosening the hatchcovers the floats might have surfaced, but not for some time, days and days, perhaps. A miracle, then? Possibly, but one worked through the agency of Ralph. Ralph the next-of-kinless, whose posthumous award, if there was to be one, would go to either a remote auntie, or to whatever waifs' and strays' home he was brought up in and simply added to the Old Boys' Roll of Honour, to be stared blindly at by generations of hungry orphans waiting for their dinner. . . .

But we had still to recover the floats. Many people imagine that when one is adrift in boats or rafts the ocean must seem a vast expanse of lonely waste. It is lonely, yes, but never vast. One's horizon is limited to a few miles at the most and when in a trough it is of course only a few yards. So if the floats had drifted far we should have had no idea where to look for them. As it happened, however, when dawn came we could see them bobbing about, four of them, two or three hundred yards away. They appeared and disappeared as our boats and rafts, also the floats themselves, rose and fell.

Captain Wilson ordered all boats to pull for the floats and this we did, each boat towing two rafts full of men. It was thigh-aching, bone-cracking work, especially for those of us who had been pulling an oar all night. I had grown bored with baling after two hours of it so had changed places with an oarsman and had now been rowing for six hours. My muscles ached painfully; my feet, being continually in the water which swished about in the bottom of the boat, were numb; my behind was sore with saltwater and friction. With great difficulty we rounded up and secured the floats with boats' painters, passing the ropes through the big rings on the tops. Actually the rings were on the bottoms, for securing them to the upper meshes of the boom-defence nets, but as the floats were upside down now, bottoms were tops.

We were certainly grateful for these giant's building bricks—as they seemed to be. As soon as it had become light the captain had had a counting of heads which revealed that there were two hundred and forty men in the four boats, forty on the eight rafts and six on two Carley floats, making a total of two hundred and eighty-six survivors out of the original three hundred and sixty. Seventy-four men had been either blasted to bits, drowned, or because wounded, torn to pieces and eaten by sharks. It might have been worse, some inevitable philosopher said. It might also have been a lot better had fewer men been sailing on the *Astrid,* for it was now proved that the lifesaving equipment was inadequate to meet the needs of so many men. The boats each contained about sixty men, yet according to a Ministry of Transport rule boats of the size carried by the *Astrid* were supposed to accommodate only forty men apiece. All the rafts now in use were also overloaded. Had the seventy four men not been killed there would have been no room for them either in the boats or on the rafts. There had been a mistake somewhere. It didn't even work out on paper, though perhaps they hadn't counted on more than half the crew and troops being left alive to save if the ship was sunk? It was difficult to know just how their minds worked. Sometimes it was impossible to tell whose side they were on.

Having secured the floats, most of the Royal Marines and a few of the more rugged soldiers transferred themselves to them from the boats. Many of the soldiers who had spent the night on the rafts now climbed into the boats, and those of us who had been rowing all night took their places. With the exception of Akbar, all the lascars were now in the boats and this was the best place for them, most of them being too weak or frightened to do anything to help themselves.

At first it was a pleasant novelty to be sitting motionless in cool blue water which came up to our knees. There were ten of us on a raft designed for six, hence its lowness in the water. We sat five a side, facing one another with our feet in the well which ran down the centre of the raft. Ten men from each boat had climbed onto the four floats, but the boats were still overburdened, and now that the captain had ordered the sails to be hoisted, mainly to attract attention, there was even less room in them. So the rafts remained as crowded as before.

I had given away my chequered Australian lumberjacket—not without regret—to a small, naked, untanned soldier as soon as the sun began to beat hotly down upon us. My shirt went to preserve the lily-whiteness of an R.A.F. body which I cursed for not having accustomed itself to the tropical sun gradually. My lifejacket was on a soldier, a non-swimmer who had been afraid of falling off his Carley float in the night, and who now refused to give it back to me, saying that it had been his all the time. He looked ill and badly frightened so I didn't argue, but I was glad that I'd cut away the canvas pouch containing my paybook and English one pound note before giving him the jacket. It was now fastened onto my belt. My plimsolls had come off while I was rowing and someone had no doubt baled them out of the boat, so that now my total possessions were one pair of khaki shorts, a belt and knife, and the canvas pouch.

The other gunners, with whom I'd had disjointed conversations when our boats jostled, seemed to be unhurt, except for George who had been swimming towards a raft when the second torpedo struck the *Astrid*. The explosion had jarred his spine badly and he had only just been able to haul himself out of the water.

Needless to say, with the sails set we made little progress—
not that we were heading anywhere in particular, unless Captain
Wilson vaguely hoped we might eventually make St. Paul, an
island several hundred miles westward to which Brazilian politic-
ians were sometimes exiled. We had in fact drifted in that direction
about forty miles, we discovered later, and in doing so we had
crossed the Line. I wondered if Neptune would endorse my Crossing-the-Line certificate if he knew I'd done it on a raft this time.

VI

THAT MORNING every man was issued with a wad of pemmican, a highly concentrated beef-extract, about the size of a thumb-
nail. The stuff was filling, but to me not satisfying, though some
of the men seemed to enjoy it. I felt as if I'd had a seven course
breakfast consisting entirely of oxo cubes. No water was issued
as this was extremely scarce and the captain decided that we
should save it in case we were adrift for more than a few days. It
was not known at the time that man can drink small amounts
of sea-water without deleterious effects, and the boats were not
equipped, as some were later in the war, with apparatus for distillation. So we just sat and thirsted as the sun crawled in the
burning sky towards its zenith.

The first time I glanced towards the other rafts I had a pleasant shock. There, on one of them, sitting almost to attention, his
whites dazzling in the sun as he sheltered under his great mush-
room of a topee, was Ordinary Signalman Pauncefort-Dundas—
complete with monocle.

I waved and shouted to him. He raised his pith helmet in a
dignified, Livingstonian manner and said loudly :

"Good morning. I trust you slept well ?"

For answer I gave him the matelot's salute, a ribald version
of the V-sign.

On my raft were four R.A.F. men, one of them a Catholic who
prayed incessantly and told his beads with frenzied rapidity; two
Fleet Air Arm ratings; Akbar the serang; one of the two apprentices—a youth of seventeen; one Army corporal; myself. The
corporal's rank was distinguished by the two white, untanned
stripes on his upper arm. On board ship the army N.C.O.s had
been obliged to wear their badges of rank fastened to their arms
with elastic bands, even while sunbathing. This amused the less formal Navy and merchant seamen on the *Astrid* and we laughed it to
scorn as typical Army bull, for all the soldiers knew one another.

I soon began to wish myself back in one of the boats, or better still, on one of the floats. The Marines and soldiers on them seemed to have room to stretch out their limbs and they all seemed to be keeping fairly dry. One of them told me afterwards that the bouncing motion took some getting used to; all of them suffered from headaches and violent sickness at first.

Owing to the overcrowding the rafts were easily overbalanced so that if anyone tried to stretch himself we were all suddenly pitched into the sea. We treated this as a joke at first and one or two of us swam around, partly to show off, but also for the relief it gave to our cramped muscles. When the cry of "shark" went up and we saw several slender black fins moving in our direction, cutting through the surface of the glazed blue water, we quickly scrambled back onto the raft and sat pressed together, watching the sharks with curiosity. One seven-footer, guided by his pilot fish, encircled our raft then dived and suspended himself about four feet below the well of the raft, so that we could look down and see his great body hanging there in the deep blue.

"Give 'im a poke wiv the bloody paddle," said the cockney corporal. "It gets on me nerves ter see 'im 'angin' abaht like that."

I pushed the paddle down between the struts and touched the sensitive tip of the shark's dorsal fin. He shot away, down into the deeper blue, and that was the last we saw of him.

When all the sharks had cleared off some men from the boats went for a swim, chiefly to stretch themselves and to relieve their bladders, for many were unable to urinate through sitting for a long time in cramped positions, and were suffering from acute stomach pains. There was no wind now and the sea was as smooth as blue wine. No doubt we were drifting, as the currents in these parts were strong, but there was little danger of being left behind if one went for a bathe. Swimming and floating with the knowledge that there were perhaps two or three miles of water beneath gave me an odd, light-headed feeling that I was flying, but in an element much stranger, more mysterious than that of the birds. I became excited at this thought during one bathe, swam too fast, nearly exhausted myself and only just made the distance back to the raft without help. I was really very tired but being keyed up had not realized it until called to make an extra physical effort. I didn't go swimming after this scare and when I did accidentally fall into the water—which was fairly often, as I occupied a place at one end of the raft—I clambered back on as quickly as possible.

At noon we were hauled alongside our boat, given one small chocolate each and a teaspoonful of water from one of the barricoes. The water was issued in cigarette tins with only one man's ration poured into each of them at a time, to save the men from the temptation to drink more than their share from a common drinking vessel. It was of course a slow method as there were only a dozen empty tins and the individual water rations had to be carefully measured, but it probably saved a lot of quarrelling.

"What about afters?" someone in the boat asked, trying to be funny.

"No afters to-day. All befores," answered the second mate.

"Dead witty," murmured a fluted Welsh voice. "Killing, man."

Our meal ended we were allowed to drift out to the end of our tether again and sit out the long afternoon in the broiling sun. At least our nether parts were cool, for the waves lapped continually round the seats of our trousers. I felt like a merman : one half of me belonged to the sky and wind, the other to the sea. I looked down at my feet, white like two jellyfish against the blue-wine water. I wondered if we should suffer from immersion foot afterwards—not that I knew what immersion foot was, really. But it sounded rather horrible : spongy, soggy, prehaps peeling. I tried not to think about it.

Nobody on the raft spoke much. Each man seemed preoccupied with thoughts of his home and people, and the chances of being able to see them again. The Catholic prayed earnestly, most of the time inaudibly now but occasionally shrieking :

"Holy Mary, Mother of God, have mercy on me for my sins!"

Every time he screamed like this he would be shouted down by the rest of us, sickened by the appalling noise, shocked and embarrassed at the egotistical self-pity of the man. While I hated to see this wretched man grovelling before God, stripping off his reserve layer by layer before our eyes, I knew that some part of me was enjoying the spectacle of someone more frightened than myself. It made me feel morally superior, yet half-ashamed of this ascendency. The man was roundly cursed when he stood up suddenly and shouted :

"Land ! I can see land !"

He pointed wildly to the westward. The raft capsized and after we had struggled back onto it the apprentice turned ferociously on the R.A.F. man :

"You bloody fool! Don't you know we're a thousand miles from land in that direction, apart from a piddling little island *you* wouldn't see anyhow? Yonder's a cloudbank. Take a good look at it in case you see any more, then you won't get excited and chuck us all in the drink again."

This was the only time the apprentice spoke on the raft. His face looked pale and drawn, his blue eyes red-rimmed and bloodshot. Although only seventeen he looked twenty-four or five years old. The sea matures men young, but as a kind of compensation it seems to preserve them from the more obvious signs of senility until they are really ancient mariners.

The R.A.F. man went into a deep sulk after the apprentice's violent outburst. He sat looking gloomily at the long low cloud-bank. I looked at it too.

"Wind," I said to Akbar.

"Yes, Sahib, and rain too, may be. We catch heavy storm to-night," he answered.

The Catholic fell to praying noisily and fervently upon hearing these words, and I wished I hadn't said anything to Akbar. I was only showing off my storm-sense anyway. At five o'clock by the corporal's watch—mine had stopped, ruined with saltwater which had got inside and I had thrown it away—we were hauled in to the boat's side again, given a smudge of pemmican each, and pushed off. There was now quite a lot of movement on the sea's surface. A wind certainly had sprung up as I'd forecast. The boats' sails were hauled down and we all sat shivering, waiting for the rain and darkness to fall upon us.

Both came suddenly and the wind in fitful gusts whitened the wavetops. The rafts rocked madly and the rain came down in thimblesful. We sat with faces uplifted and mouths wide open. The rain tasted like tepid water from a cistern, not particularly refreshing. In the boats they were catching it in buckets, balers and empty cigarette tins, but we on the rafts had nothing but our mouths and it was neck-breaking work holding our heads back. We soon gave it up, seeming to lose our thirsts, and sat, the rain streaming off our bodies, watching the luminous plankton spilling over our legs as waves broke on the raft. I realized what a living thing the sea really is. However glassy and dead it seemed by day, at night it glowed with life as if the stars had exploded and the bits had fallen into the ocean, there to live on forever with a luminous uncertainty weaving interminable patterns of shifting light for no one to set eyes on except a few ship-wrecked men and millions of uninterested fish.

Down below our feet, miles down on the sea-floor, strange plants, seaflowers lived, fed, propagated, died, and all for what? I stared down into the well of the raft, expecting to find the answer suddenly, in a blinding flash. Surely in such a plight as this *something* should be revealed to a man? He should emerge with at least fresh moral insight, having lived close to people stripped of their everyday affectations. But all I seemed to be aware of that night, the longest of my life, was the devastating effect that waiting, just waiting, has on the human soul. Never since have I purposely made anyone wait.

Captain Wilson had ordered those with lights on their kapok

jackets to switch them on so that the boats could keep in touch with one another, but by ten o'clock it was raining bamboo curtains and visibility was arm's length only. Ten o'clock, the corporal had said it was. He had a watch with a luminous, planktonic dial. Ten o'clock, and I'd thought it must be near dawn. My mind had become a vernier of the night, slowed time down almost to a standstill. Time, Shakespeare had said, must have a stop. We were getting near it, the Universe was running down. Quick, someone, fetch the key and wind it up! What's the time now, Corp? Five past ten. But hours ago you said it was ten o'clock! You must have stopped. Quick, Corporal, the key, find the key and wind it up! What's the time now, Corp? He doesn't answer. Lean across and shake him. The time, Corporal? Aw shutup for Christ's sake, I jus told yer! But that was ages ago. Naw, it was jus now, so shutup for Christ's sake! Wind it up, Corp, for God's sake wind it up! Don't let it stop, don't let it stop! But time *must* have a stop. When? Later. Not in my time.

Urine surged involuntarily out of my body. I felt its warmth for an instant about my belly, then it was gone. I shuddered as the seeming last therms left me, like fleas the dying dog. They died from exposure. It sounded like photographic jargon. They died from being left out in the rain all night like washing, soggy, shapeless, disgusting. I felt disgusting, spongy. Death by immersion, from the sea and the sky. They suffered from immersion body ever afterwards. Death by mermanship. I was half a fish already, sitting thigh-high in water. I remembered a petrifying waterfall, Mother Shipton's, somewhere in Yorkshire. Things hung under its constant drip and turned to stone in a few months : umbrellas, garden tools, stuffed birds, teddy bears. Human beings? As a normal, healthy child I had wondered. Now I knew. I was turning to stone, like the victims of Medusa and Mother Shipton.

My left hand tightly gripped the paddle while my right hand and arm supported the apprentice who had fallen into a fit of unconsciousness which could hardly be called sleep. I was trying to stop him from tumbling backwards off the raft and upsetting it, but I didn't succeed. Seven times during the night we were flung off, and each time we heaved ourselves back onto it. After the third time I decided to haul us in to the boat to see if they could take the apprentice for someone who wasn't so exhausted. I took hold of the line and heaved. All I got was fifty yards of line. We were adrift from our boat; the line must not have been secured properly; it had worked loose and snaked off over the gunwale in the rainy darkness; nobody had noticed it. But the boats couldn't be far away. I dropped the line over the side and didn't tell the others. They were all huddled together now, like animals defeated by a storm, a soggy scrum of bodies. I put my head down too, and closed my eyes. The rain drummed madly on my taut, naked back.

VII

As the first light of dawn streaked the western sky the rain stopped. The sun rose, the sky became blue and the sea turned from grey-green into liquid lapis lazuli again. We stretched our stiff, agonized bodies and tried to see where the other boats and rafts were. Soon a Fleet Air Arm man spotted one of the floats, then I saw another. Shortly afterwards our boat appeared, looking for us. They came alongside, secured our rope, gave us pemmican and one piece of chocolate.

"And that," said the second mate, "is more or less the end of the rations in this boat. Let's see what there is on the raft."

We clambered stiffly and shakily into the boat and as the raft regained its full buoyancy Akbar raised the wooden seating. In between the buoyancy tanks was another compartment half full of water in which floated two tins of chocolate and a tin of biscuits. We handed them to the second who put them in the boat's locker.

"There is water in tank, too," Akbar said.

He put a brown hand into the tank and brought out a cupped palmful of water. He drank, then spat, screwing up his face like a monkey's.

"Salt! Sea get into it," he said.

"Well, it doesn't matter. We all got enough water through our pores last night to carry us on for a few days, I should think." the second answered.

"What about a swop-over, some of these bods doing a spell on the raft for a change?" suggested one of the Fleet Air Arm men who had been on the raft for twenty-four hours.

The second mate looked round the boat.

"All right," he said. "Who'll volunteer?"

The men in the boat looked the other way. Nobody spoke.

"What about you blokes in the bows?" the second nodded towards three Army sergeants who were huddled together in the fore part of the boat. "None of you three has pulled an oar yet. Suppose you swop with some of these chaps on the raft for a few hours?"

"I'm sick," moaned one of the sergeants, drawing a blanket up over his face, while the other two just sat with eyes downcast.

"Huh!" snorted the second. "Fine example some o' you N.C.O.s are!"

An R.A.F. corporal moved over to the side of the boat where the raft was.

"I'll change with somebody," he said.

We left the apprentice in the boat and clambered back onto the raft with the volunteer, the only volunteer.

"Bloody rotten shower o' bastards," muttered the Catholic as he climbed aboard the raft.

It was the first time I'd heard him swear at anybody. At least it was a change from hearing him pray. They had made room in the stern sheets of the boat for the apprentice, who was now in bad shape, to lie down. The second had the sail hoisted again and steered towards the other boats, floats and rafts which had managed to re-form into our pathetic, drifting convoy in little. I could see Captain Wilson holding the tiller of his boat and looking dreadfully haggard. He was wearing a new kind of rubber exposure suit which I hadn't seen before, and as he seemed to be the only possessor of one I gathered that it was his private property. Later these yellow suits became issued gear to some merchant seamen, though I never saw any DEMS gunners with them. They were two-piece, very light, and rolled up easily into a small pack. I didn't begrudge the captain his now, though I should have preferred to have spent the previous night in one rather than in my bare skin as I had done. But I wasn't bothered by sunburn as some of the men were and I revelled in the hot morning sunrays which seemed to go right into my bones, pouring warm oil into the joints—all those above water, that is. Like everyone's on the rafts, my feet looked and felt like blubber through being constantly in the water. I gazed down at them : two jellyfish in a tank of blue fire. The R.A.F. corporal who had just come onto the raft with us had an idea.

"Each lift your feet out of the water and rest them across somebody's knees for a short spell," he suggested, "then somebody else can massage them."

We tried this and it created some interest, besides bringing the life back to our feet. I looked at the man who had thought of it. He was about thirty, with a pleasant, rugged face and had the assured look of a man who has knocked about the world a bit.

"Are you a Regular?" I asked him.

He shook his head.

"Not likely. I had all sorts of jobs before the war. Used to travel around. Once went broke in North Africa. Lived on bananas for three months," he grinned, "I couldn't even eat one now."

One of the Fleet Air Arm brought out a small diary from his pocket and began to dry the leaves.

"Good," said Akbar, "you dry paper then we all have a smoke. I got tobacco."

We all looked at him. All the cigarette supply had been doled out and smoked up during the first night adrift. Akbar fished out an oilskin pouch with about an ounce of black, pipe-tobacco in it.

"See!" he triumphed.

In a few minutes the diary was dry and we began to roll cigarettes very carefully, trying not to get them wet. Larry, the ex-banana eater, had a cigarette lighter which still worked. We lit our fat, disintegrating cigarettes and Akbar chuckled at the expressions on our faces as we tried to suck down the venomous smoke without choking. Akbar smoked happily in his own fashion : holding the cigarette between the second and third fingers of his right hand, cupping both hands round it and drawing through the space between his thumbs. His religion, he explained, forbade his lips touching tobacco, but there were ways of circumventing the prohibition, and this was one of them. He suggested that I should try his method and I did so, really to see if the tobacco tasted any better. It was much worse, seeming to have the odour of smoked, salted flesh mingled with the tobacco's natural foulness. I quietly flipped the cigarette away and hoped that Akbar wouldn't offer me any more of his "makings." The others were also dropping their tattered fags furtively over the side and probably hoping the same.

All that afternoon we sat without moving or speaking, staring dully at the dragon-fly-blue water. For my part I could almost say that I sat without thinking either. As evening drew near and the day cooled we began to liven up a bit. Our raft was pulled in to the boat and we were issued with half a small biscuit and one chocolate each. The second officer was looking very wearied and some of the men in the boat were suffering from sunburn.

"What are our chances of being picked up?" I managed to ask the Second without the others hearing.

He shook his head and made a gesture of hopeless resignation.

"We're not on any regular route. If anything sees us it'll be by accident—a ship off course, or a plane, maybe."

As we drifted off from the boat and the Catholic began his interminable vespers I was overwhelmed with gloom and fear of the coming night. I watched the horizon climb and swallow the sun. I saw the stars come out like mice, one by one, and plankton glow in green, shifting patterns.

There was even less animation on the raft now. All sat with heads sunk on chests or buried in arms, slouched forward and resting on wet, bare knees, not asleep but in a salt sea-doze. All except Akbar, and myself. He sat upright, opposite me now, calm, serene as death. Yes, it is as if he is dead, I thought. Soon, to-morrow, or the next day we shall all be dead. We will just drop off this raft, one by one, and slip away quietly into the depths of blue midnight down below. I didn't mind very much now. All I wanted to do was to sleep, the longer the better. My eyes were beginning to close down and I was swaying backwards. A hand caught at my arm and jerked me forwards again. I found Akbar's face looking intently into mine and in the moonlight the man's teeth gleamed between his taut lips.

"Do not go to sleep, Gunner-Sahib," he said quietly. "In sleep there is danger."

"What does it matter?" I yawned.

"To-morrow, we shall get help," Akbar said simply.

"What makes you think so?"

Akbar looked at me with his old, patient eyes.

"You are Christian man?" he asked.

I didn't want to talk about religion. Perhaps I'm an atheist—until I'm scared, I thought.

"It says C. of E. on my paybook," I answered flippantly. "It has to say something so that they know what sort of a hole to put you in if you get killed ashore."

The time to be religious was when you had least need of religion. Then you had more to give, and less to take.

"Pardon?" said Akbar, looking puzzled.

"Nothing," I answered.

"I am Mohammedan," he announced.

"I gathered you were."

"Every night I look towards the east, and I pray."

"Yes."

"To-night I pray very hard, very long time."

"Good."

I hoped he would do it very, very quietly. Perhaps he had done it already. One couldn't tell by the tense.

"To-morrow, we get help," Akbar reaffirmed.

As simple as that. To-morrow. And how many days had we been adrift now? Two? Three? I didn't know. Time, which takes survey of all the world, had given us a miss.

It was in fact our third night without a ship. Finned shapes glided beneath my green-white feet. I gazed down into a night-mare of luminous shadows, deep-water phantoms and flickering small-fry shoals. All this unnecessary Creation, I thought, as my mind sank down, down into the depths.

The sun beat upon my back and shoulders. I tried to straighten up but found it impossible at first. By degrees, as if I were straightening a steel spring, I managed to get the kink out of my spine and neck. It was agonizing, but I did not suffer alone. All the other men, except Akbar who had not, apparently, slept, were groaning, cursing and writhing in private waking hells. A fair breeze was blowing and a few white clouds were being puffed along by it through the tropical blue heavens. There was quite a bit of movement in everything afloat now, and I found it faintly exhilarating. I started to move my legs to bring some life to them, but stopped short. The cockney corporal was missing.

"Where's the Corp?" I asked Akbar.

He did not answer at once, but just looked at me, then he said :

"Soldier die in night. Have bad wound in back, but say nothing about it. Just slip off raft. Sharks have him now, I think."

We were stunned.

"Did he say anything? Was he able to speak, I mean?" I said. Akbar nodded.

"He say, 'Good-bye, chum. Room for one more now, sitting room only'. I do not know what last part mean, but soldier call me 'chum'. I am coloured man. No white man call me 'chum' before."

He smiled, half to himself. Death knows no colour-bar, perhaps he was thinking.

We reported the corporal's death and departure to the second officer when we were hauled alongside the boat and given a chocolate breakfast, the last of the rations. He nodded but said nothing. It was not indifference, nor callousness, but resignation. Two wounded men had died in the boat during the night and had been put over the side. Sharks had torn them out of the men's grasps. Others, too, would soon be shark food, judging by the number of apparently lifeless forms draped over the thwarts and gunwales. One soldier was covered with huge blisters, some of which had burst, leaving great patches of raw flesh. Salt spray on these parts must have been torture to the poor man.

We sat out the timeless golden morning and by noon were all in a dazed, talkless state. There was now not a scrap of food between the lot of us, but we were all too enfeebled to care much about that. I was sitting, head in hands, staring down at the bottomless blue water beneath my feet, when I thought I heard the sound of an aircraft engine. I looked up and saw that others were staring up into the sky, shielding their eyes from the sun with their hands. A few in the boats were trying to stand up on the thwarts and, not being strong enough to keep their balance, falling off again. The sound grew more distant. It was a plane all right, but where?

Soon, out of the sun it seemed, came the glorious form of a

Sunderland flying boat. At first I didn't believe it. I rubbed my eyes until they smarted with salt. The aircraft had turned south, away from us, showing a gleaming silver profile, appearing to sail, rather than fly—a true ship of the air. Again she altered course, and then again, this time coming towards us. The men in the boats stood up and waved scraps of clothing; a rocket zoomed upwards from the captain's boat; another from the first mate's, but the Sunderland turned away, not seeing us. More rockets. The flying boat altered course, towards us again, this time flashing an aldis. They had seen us! She came in low, a great, roaring silver sky-ship, looking more closely at us, then circled, flashing signals which I couldn't read. The captain was standing up in his boat, semaphoring B-R-I-T-I-S-H with two handkerchieves while somebody held his legs to steady him. The flying boat suddenly jettisoned the two depth-charges we had seen under her wings as she passed overhead.

"She's going to try to land!" shouted one of the Fleet Air Arm men on the raft, and there were muffled booms followed by mushrooms of water as the charges exploded at seventy-five feet.

I gathered that this jettisoning of the depth-charges was a precautionary measure taken when the landing was going to be rough.

"She'll never make it!" one of the other men shouted.

"It is sent by Mary, Mother of God!" the Catholic exclaimed, crossing himself swiftly, expertly, without taking his eyes off the Sunderland.

Akbar smiled.

"Allah be praised," he said.

The aircraft came in low, skimming the waves, trying to settle, but it was no good. She bounced dangerously off the sea's broken surface like a huge, daredevil surf-rider.

"Take her up! Take her up again!" one of the airmen shouted from the raft.

As if the pilot had heard, the flying boat began to climb rapidly and encircled us, flashing the lamp, her wet hull glistening. There was no need to try to read the message. She couldn't land; the sea was too rough. She turned towards us and zoomed overhead. We cheered and waved as the plane sped away, dropping something as it went, something which splashed and dyed the water bright green all round it. All the boats rowed towards the object, dragging the rafts and floats. The captain's boat reached it first. It was a small float and cylinder which had contained the marker dye; inside the float was a message, hurriedly scrawled on a piece of signal-pad paper: SORRY. CAN'T MAKE IT. THUMBS UP THOUGH. THE NAVY'LL SOON BE HERE.

Captain Wilson read the message aloud to his own boat then passed it on to the officers in charge of the others.

"All we have to do now is wait," said the second mate to us, after reading the message.

"Wotcha fink we bin doin' all this time?" asked one of the scorched soldiers.

Everybody laughed inordinately, hysterically almost, and light-headedly shook hands with people whose faces they had hated only a few minutes before, and would no doubt hate again in a day or two, after the novelty of being rescued had worn off. Now that we had had the news of an almost certain rescue everybody was happy. I tried to have a swim but found myself sinking as soon as I let go of the raft, being too weak to use my arms or legs much, so I contented myself with hanging onto the grab-lines and stretching my body. When shark fins appeared I quickly climbed back onto the raft and watched them glide by with their blue pilots. At about five o'clock we sighted smoke on the horizon.

"That was quick work," said Larry. "There must have been a Navy ship close by."

"Boy, am I going to get drunk as soon as I get ashore," said the Catholic, no longer afraid, no longer at prayer.

We stared at him first in amazement, then with disgust, contempt, and perhaps a little pity.

It was not the Navy. As the ship hove in sight we could see she was a merchantman of some five or six thousand tons, and she did not seem to be British. She approached us cautiously and we sat in silence, wondering if she were an allied or an enemy vessel, an armed raider, for instance. She carried quite a lot of deck cargo which might have concealed 4- or 6-inch guns. On the ship we could see sailors staring down at us, so we stared back and said nothing. Suddenly a voice hailed us from the bridge:

"Are you British?"

"Yes!" came back a great, hoarse chorus.

Immediately there was a cheer from the merchantman's decks, then their captain's voice came down again:

"Please excuse our caution. We are Greeks. We did not know if you were our allies or not."

"We weren't sure about you either," shouted up Captain Wilson. "But didn't the R.A.F. give you our position?"

The Greek captain sounded puzzled.

"The R.A.F.? We have not seen aircraft since we left Free-town."

"Where are you bound for?"

"Cape Town."

"Most of these men are for the Cape and farther east. Can

you take some of them? We have wounded and sick men who need attention at once."

"Yes, but we must hurry. It will soon be dark and there may be U-boats."

"I understand. Some of my crew and the naval ratings will remain here until the Royal Navy arrives, otherwise they will not know what has happened to us."

The Greek came closer and let down scramble-nets up which the soldiers, airmen, and lascars climbed as fast as their weak conditions allowed them to. The wounded men and those badly sun-burned were taken aboard in stretchers slung from the derricks, then the Greeks started to haul the rafts aboard the ship as extra life-saving equipment. I watched the raft on which I'd spent three days go aloft with a curious affection. The whole operation took time and it was quite dark by the time it was finished. Those of us who were left in the boats numbered about eighty and included the *Astrid's* officers and gunners, the Fleet Air Arm men and the Royal Marines. We sprawled, about twenty to a boat, in comparative comfort. The ship was a sitting duck for any U-boat and we admired the Greek captain for the efficient, yet seemingly unhurried manner in which he conducted the rescue work.

The ship's cook threw down some loaves and I heard that a bottle of whisky had been passed down, but neither bread nor whisky did I taste, it all disappearing long before we had even left the ship's side. But I didn't mind. I felt safe and certain now of rescue, the boat was dry and seemed like an ark after the raft, so I prepared to bed down for the night under a sail. This was the third mate's boat I had climbed into and he sat, a piratical figure with a red handkerchief tied round his head, at the tiller. Ordinary Signalman Pauncefort-Dundas was in this boat too, but no longer the immaculate, sea-going Higher Civil Servant. He had lost his topee and was shirtless, though he still had his monocle. It shone glassily in the moonlight. He looked dreadfully haggard and as bony as an old horse, but much more real than I'd ever seen him look before.

"You look quite human," I told him frankly.

"I wish I felt it," he sighed, then shuddered. "It's so terribly cold."

"Try some of this sail," I suggested.

He crawled thankfully under part of it and lay jerking and shivering, but uncomplaining. He had asked for all this. He could have had a nice soft job ashore, or perhaps never even left his comfortable office in the Ministry of String—or whatever department he hailed from. He had made his bed, as they say, and was lying on it—without a murmur. Here was a man.

I closed my eyes and thanked God for our small comforts, which seemed so large. The third had lashed the tiller, all the boats were secured to one another, so we all lay stretched on thwarts and side-benches, rocking in the gentle swell.

I awoke in hot sunlight, at about eight o'clock. There was very little wind and we rolled gently in a smooth blue sea. The third mate was still asleep near the tiller, while next to me Pauncefort-Dundas stirred himself and clambered rheumatically out of the sail's folds. He yawned unobtrusively and wedged his monocle firmly in position.

"I say, that's the best sleep I ever had, as far as I can remember," he said to me.

I agreed that it would take some beating for me, too. Ordinary Signalman Pauncefort-Dundas looked less haggard but a little more gaunt than usual, otherwise he seemed quite fit. The other men in the boats were waking up and stretching their limbs. Pauncefort-Dundas stood on one of the thwarts and stared at the horizon.

"You know, I do believe there's a ship coming towards us," he announced quite placidly.

"Where? Where? Where?" came voices from the boat.

The signalman pointed a long finger to the north-east.

"There," he said.

We stood on thwarts and strained our eyes. Yes, a ship was approaching. To us she looked as big as a cruiser, her size was so exaggerated by our low position. I thought she was probably a destroyer : she turned out to be a corvette. We cheered hoarsely as she drew alongside and I noticed an officer on the bridge taking ciné-pictures. One of the matelots in the boat made a rude gesture into the camera's eye which was no doubt censored if the film was for public showing, but deliberately retained if for the wardroom. Scramble-nets were unrolled and we climbed them like old tired monkeys. On deck we formed a line and shuffled forward, first towards a petty officer who took our names, ranks and numbers, then on to another P.O. who handed us a tot of rum—the Navy's panacea. Lastly, after we had swallowed the fiery spirit, on to the cook and his assistant who ladled thick, scalding soup into thick mugs and thrust them at us. What a breakfast ! Several men were sick before they got to the soup, the rum being too much for their weak stomachs. I marvelled that they had anything to be sick with and secretly hoped that they were the ones who had pinched all the bread the night before.

As I stood smugly sipping the cook's hell-broth, the twin pom-poms suddenly opened fire on the boom-defence tanks, with the object of sinking them so that they were not a shipping danger.

But the blast from the guns blew the steaming soup right into my face and jammed the mug tightly over my mouth and chin. I ran up and down the deck like a muzzled mastiff, pulling at the mug, while even the tiredest survivor laughed.

Ordinary Signalman Pauncefort-Dundas, dressed only in shorts and monocle, had been greeted with restrained enthusiasm by the corvette's crew who at first mistook him for a commissioned officer. Then, as he had climbed slowly but with great dignity up the scramble-netting, and over the ship's rail, the crew had been told that he was just "one of the boys." Then he was cheered wildly and slapped so heartily on the back that he nearly collapsed. But already, now the excitement had died down, there were rumours spreading about the signalman. He was really an admiral pretending to be a matelot so that he could see how the other half lived. (This speculation was no doubt based on a yarn I had heard in barracks about an admiral who periodically went through the "joining ship" routine disguised as an Able-Seaman to see if the chiefs and P.O.s were doing their jobs properly. It had always sounded like a sailor's hammock-dream to me, but there may have been some truth in it. Admirals are in a position to be eccentric, after all). Another rumour had it that Pauncefort-Dundas was a wealthy earl with a castle in Scotland and four Rolls-Royces, but he was a bit touched and thought he was broke so he joined the Navy. Yet a third school hailed him as a penniless viscount, seeing the world as a matelot—because he hadn't any pennies. A fourth claimed him to be a secret service agent, an M.I.5 type disguised as an English Gentleman masquerading as a British matelot. Subtle, the last one.

After the pom-poms had put paid to our very useful floats and they had sunk to the bottom of the deep blue sea, the four ship's boats were roped in line ahead and towed by the corvette, but it was not long before the first boat shipped water and sank to her gunwales. The towing cable parted and wrapped itself round the propeller, so that the ship, after only an hour's steaming away from the spot where she had picked us up, came to a sudden, definite, and depressing stop.

The survivors sprawled about the fore-deck as members of the crew tried to clear the fouled screw while the corvette undulated in the gentle swell. Most of the men lying on the deck were fast asleep so knew nothing of the trouble. I wished that I, too, were blissfully unaware, but I was all too conscious of the fact that we were a sitting target for torpedoes. But there was nothing we could do about it, so why worry? Better to cocoon myself in the blanket I'd just been issued, and go to sleep. After half an hour or so, I did.

I awoke about two hours later to the welcome throb of the engines. We were under way again. There was life in the ship, wonderful, throbbing, pulsating life! Circling the water-logged boats, we shot them up and sank them before the ship's bows headed for the place we had set out from, Freetown.

"Well," said Captain Wilson as he came on to the fo'c'sle to talk to his fellow-survivors from the *Astrid*, "how did you like our Crossing-the-Line ceremony?"

"Do you mean that we actually drifted over it, sir?" one of the men asked.

"Just," answered the captain, handing round cigarettes. "We were just south of the Line when they picked us up. Must have drifted about thirty-five miles. The currents are pretty strong round these parts. Well, it'll be something to tell your grand-children."

He grinned and strolled away, smoking. A bos'n's pipe pierced the air, followed by a strong voice shouting:

"Hands to dinner! Hands to dinner!"

None of the blanketed figures huddled about the deck moved, although most of them were now awake, smoking luxuriously.

"That means you blokes," said the sailor who had just piped dinner. "We ain't got no special pipes for survivors. Just don't eat *all* the grub, that's all!"

Lured by the promise, then the smell of food, we trooped down to the mess-deck and had our first meal for five days. It consisted of thick soup, bread, bully beef, with rice pudding for "afters." Then cups and cups of tea. The corvette's crew went cheerfully about, serving us with as much food as we could eat, and calling everybody gannets, the Navy's favourite word for gluttons. Actually we didn't gormandize much. Most of the men were well-contented with the first helping given to them and some couldn't eat all of that, their stomachs and digestive systems being out of condition. After dinner we went back on deck to sleep away the afternoon.

At five o'clock I woke up wonderfully refreshed and helped to coal the galley. This meant bringing buckets of coal up from out of a bunker, carrying them along the deck to the galley, then tipping them into a bin or bunker beside the stove. Long before it was full I was completely exhausted and asked to be allowed to rest. The P.O. cook grinned.

"Aye, that's all right, laddie. You haven't got your strength back properly yet. Go and sleep some more."

It was true. The sense of returned strength had been mainly psychological. I went back to the other survivors, another meal, and a long, deep, sleep.

VIII

DURING THE next few days, as our appetites increased, the crew of the corvette showed great patience, especially at meal times with eighty extra men feeding in two sittings. Yet only once did I see an outburst of temper when two of the crew argued with each other about washing up, or some other chore. One of the men, a wiry, ginger-headed Yorkshireman, clouted his "oppo" across the back with a large soup plate which broke, making a cut a foot long, from left deltoid to right latissimus. Blood streamed from the man's naked, bronzed, muscular back. It ended the argument. Yorky, horrified at what he had done, rushed to his friend's aid and began mopping at the blood with his handkerchief.

"Ee, ahm right sorry ah hit you, lad," he said. "Ah must've lost me temper, like, an' afore ah knew what ah were doin' t'soup plate were flyin' aht o' me 'and."

He was almost in tears. His friend patted Yorky's shoulder reassuringly.

"That's all right, mate," he said, with a strong Liverpool accent. "In fact, it's nothin' at all, whacker. It was my fault anyway."

"You can 'ave me tot when it comes oop," Yorky sobbed.

"Thanks very much," said Scouse quickly.

But when he came back from seeing the Sick Berth Attendant, a strip of plaster right across his back, he waved the penitent's proffered tot of rum aside.

"Skip it, Yorky," he said. "Sometime I'll give you a clout back instead."

Someone handed him a soup plate but he declined the offer just then.

There were two West African youths on board who had signed on as mess-boys for a couple of weeks. They were only paid about one and six a day but apparently they thought it was worth it for they certainly seemed happy enough. They were great favourites of the crew who treated them almost as pets. They were also the blackest negroes I'd ever seen, with dazzling teeth displayed in perpetual smiles and thick, muscular bodies. The Freetown boys dressed in sailor's tropical whites but went hatless and padded about in quick, bare feet. I never knew their real names, only the ones which the crew had given them: Dhobi Smalls, and Darken Ship.

Only one man on the corvette was an active service rating, or "regular" in the Navy. The majority were wartime sailors; the officers R.N.V.R., except for the captain, who was R.N.R. The officers were the only ones who wore any badges of rank most of the time; the rest of the ship's company wore sandals, shorts and pirate headgear. I liked the informality of this little ship and was sorry to leave her when we arrived in Freetown after being aboard four days.

At Freetown we said good-bye to the friends we had made both on the *Astrid* and on the corvette. The Royal Marines and Fleet Air Arm boys were sent straight to the big depot ship anchored in the bay, the *Astrid's* officers and Captain Wilson went ashore to an hotel, while we, the seven DEMS gunners, were packed off to the grammar school. This had been taken over by an Australian padre and his wife for receiving Merchant Navy survivors. I thought it rather odd that we should be sent here, rather than straight to the depot ship—where I was sure we should end up—and suspected it was another instance of the Navy's not knowing quite what to do with DEMS ratings. I looked forward without enthusiasm to another tedious round of misunderstandings and endless explanations, but it was not really so bad.

The grammar school—like most grammar schools—was a big grey building. It had a cool, dark colonnade and stood in a large walled patio at the farthest corner of which were some outbuildings—wash-houses, lavatories and so on. I use the word *patio* because the effect of the whole was Spanish, or perhaps colonial Spanish. An aerial circus of three vultures wheeled slowly overhead, each in turn making a leisurely descent into the court to pick up pieces of bread thrown out by the padre or his wife. We didn't go beyond the colonnade into the school itself. Breakfast consisting of bacon and eggs, rolls and butter, bananas, and hot, sweet, black coffee, was laid out on trestle tables in the colonnade. While we smoked and drank cup after cup of the delicious coffee, the padre told us how he and his wife had fled before the Japanese advanced on Sumatra where they had been looking after a mission for seamen, and how they'd sailed to the Northern Territory in a native fishing vessel, together with four other Australians. They had then come to Freetown, after a short rest in Sydney, to look after survivors there. For the first time I noticed the blue and white flag of The Flying Angel Mission to Seamen hanging limply from the top of a staff in the still air of the patio.

"But we must fix you up with some clothes," said the padre in his kindly, twangling, Aussie voice.

They had no naval gear of course, but they gave us white T-shirts, khaki shorts, canvas shoes and flat, khaki topees—also shaving tackle. My cherished English one pound note was beginning to seem superfluous. We shaved and showered in the wash-house,

then changed into the new gear. Shaving was a painful operation as all of us had ten-day beards, not having bothered to try
to shave on the crowded corvette. George's back seemed better,
though he still had difficulty in bending, but as he said, he didn't
intend to complain about it in Freetown in case they kept him
there. He would wait until he got back to England then go sick.
Perhaps he would get a shore job as an instructor. My feet
appeared not to have suffered from immersion, and nobody else
had any ills. Ralph was never spoken about, though all of us—
with the exception of George—felt guilty of misjudging the man,
and I'm sure thought about him a great deal.

After our transformation we went back to smoke, drink more
coffee and play bagatelle in the shade of the porticoes. It was a
very pleasant morning. I hoped that we should perhaps be billeted
at the grammar school with the kindly padre and his wife, but
this was not to be; we were to report to the DEMS office at
noon. After thanking our hosts we set off through Kru Town to
see what Fate had in store for us. We passed a barracks where,
for some reason or other, an ensign was just being hoisted and
a band was playing the National Anthem. We stood to attention,
topees in hand, while the dirge-like strains mourned on. I was
wondering why this funereal tune, composed either by Henry
Carey in the eighteenth century, or by the Elizabethan, John Bull,
used by the Germans before the 1914-18 War under the title,
Heil dir im Siegerkranz, and by the Americans as *My Country
Tis of Thee,* should always make me feel patriotic, yet cynical,
proud, but embarrassed, when I noticed George's face, his lips
drawn back in a tight smile.

"H.M. King knows F.A. about it," he gritted between his teeth.

Then I knew that at least one other person shared my mixed
feelings. The anthem ended and the band almost at once broke
into *Hearts of Oak.* We donned topees and resumed our walk.
Some native women were washing clothes in a stream, flogging
them on the bank with bat-shaped sticks and singing rhythmically.
They stopped, stared, pointed and chortled at us in Kru talk
as we passed. Green lizards darted across our path, a mangy dog,
sniffing, followed us. We arrived, dusty, at the DEMS office.

George made his report, then the two of us who were on watch
at the Oerlikons at the time of the torpedoing, Griffiths and myself, made our reports separately. When it came to my turn I
followed the chief into the office and stood to attention before
the commander's desk.

"Relax a bit," he said, with a friendly smile. "It's too hot out
here to be formal. Sit down."

He indicated a cane chair.

"Have a cigarette?"

He pushed a box towards me. I felt as if I were in the American Navy, or the R.A.F. I sat smoking and watching the pearls of sweat forming on the officer's brow immediately after he had mopped it with a large white handkerchief.

"So you're the one who saw the U-boat?" the commander began.

I gave him a description including the approximate tonnage and armaments of the submarine, and when I mentioned the insignia, the Ace of Spades, he raised his shaggy eyebrows.

"That fellow again? We've had trouble with him before. Still, he didn't treat you badly, did he?"

"No, sir. He was very courteous."

The commander nodded.

"He usually is. Sank one ship fifteen miles off the coast near Lagos. Gave the chaps provisions and towed them in their boats to the nearest beach. They simply walked back to town."

I told him about Ralph and he listened attentively, making notes, but no comments. The interview ended and I joined the others outside. We climbed into a large brake and were driven helter-skelter down to the pier by a mad, bare-footed African who sang vigorously all the way. Survivors of the ride, bruised, breathless, thankful, we boarded a launch which took us out to the depot ship, an ex-liner, now H.M.S. *Pomfret Castle*, known to the boys as Pomfret Cake, or just the Cake, or by association, the Piece o' Cake.

From the top of the ladder a gigantic chief petty officer glowered down on us like an angry god.

"What's this party?" he bellowed at the quartermaster.

"Somebody's birthday party, looks of it," answered the Q.M.

We climbed the ladder, saluted the spotless quarter-deck, and stepped aboard. George handed the chief a chit from the DEMS office.

"Came first post this morning," he said, not smiling.

"Eh?" the chief said, reading the note and missing the point. "Oh, DEMS blokes. Well, what're you doin' in them Dr. Livingstone get-ups?"

"Waiting to get some pusser's," George answered.

We went with the chief to the stores and were given a kit-bag each, white tropical gear, one blue suit and a hammock on loan only. It was only a skeleton kit, the Jack Dusty explained.

"Cos you looks like a lot o' bleedin' skeletons," guffawed the chief.

There was in fact little clothing to spare on the *Pomfret Castle*. We would get the rest of our gear when we reached the U.K.,

we were told, and we were to live on the Cake for a few days,
reporting to the DEMS office ashore every morning, until we
were drafted to homeward bound ships as extra or relief gunners.

George had gone off to the Marines' quarters for kit and a meal,
and we went for one on the seamen's mess-deck. At night there
was no room for us to sling our hammocks; instead we spread them
on the deck after rounds and had to suffer being climbed over
and walked on as men coming off watch groped their way in the
half-light towards their hammocks. It was stiflingly hot despite
the fans, and the air-scoops which stuck out of nearly every
porthole. We lay half-naked, sweating, staring up at the bulging
hammocks above us, thinking of homeward bounders and how
long we should have to wait for them.

Next morning we reported to the DEMS office. George and
the two seamen-gunners were lucky: they were to join a ship
bound for home that very afternoon. The remaining four of us
looked at them enviously as they came out of the office with their
draft-chits and big smiles. The chief followed them out onto the
little veranda in front of the office, booming orders about collecting their gear and being ready with it at oh one double oh, etcet-
era.

"And what about us, Chief? Back to the Pomfret Cake. I suppose?" said Tom Potter.

The chief shrugged.

"Please yourselves," he said. "O' course, there's always Lumbley
Beach."

I'd heard of Lumbley. It was a beautiful beach with date palms
and almost white, hour-glass fine, sand. We had each subbed a
pound against our pay the day before, so we went down to the
cable office to send messages home, bought some food and canned
beer at the N.A.A.F.I., then hitched a lorry-lift to the beach—
after saying good-bye to George and the seamen-gunners and calling them lucky bastards.

We slept most of the day under the palm trees, going in for
swims at short intervals when we got too hot. There were a few
R.A.F. men, from the Sunderland base, at the beach, and some
middle-aged women with pale, dehydrated appearances—probably wives of British officials. They were very aloof and seemed
to stare straight through us as we passed by. They were playing
bridge in a bored, desultory way—all suffering from club-fatigue
no doubt.

In the evening we went back to the Pomfret Cake and saw
a pre-war silent film on the upper deck. The screen was placed
in the middle of the audience which meant that half of them saw
the film the other way round—traffic driving on the left side of

the road, although it was an American setting; but worse of all the sub-titles were reversed and as there was no talking in the film it was almost incomprehensible to us. We had chosen to sit on the *wrong* side of the screen, not knowing that it was a silent film.

"The only time you should sit on that side is when there's a Charlie on," a matelot informed us, "cos then it don't matter about the words. See?"

A great tribute to Chaplin's acting. Unfortunately there was never a Charlie on for us.

Before the film show started we had watched palm wine drinkards being carried aboard, some inert, some fighting drunk. Palm wine was a forbidden drink, therefore nearly everyone drank it, at least once. We took some to the beach next day and I had hallucinations all afternoon—kept seeing animals riding bicycles out of the corner of my eye. John Griffiths went into a kind of trance-state, while Tom Potter simply lay ogling the aloof Englishwomen. It had obviously affected him the worst.

Teddy Fox had been drafted to a ship that same morning. He never reached home. His ship was blown in two by a torpedo near the Azores, and though there were a dozen survivors, Teddy was not among them.

We went to the beach every day, after reporting to the DEMS office to see about drafts to ships. Apart from the N.A.A.F.I. there was no other place we could go. Three days after Teddy Fox had left, Tom and John both got a draft to a fast cargo-passenger ship, a Frenchman, bound for the U.K. I said good-bye to them, called them lucky bastards, then went to the N.A.A.F.I. and sat glumly drinking canned beer. I'd no wish to go to the beach by myself and sit looking at the bridge-playing white ladies, or even drink palm wine and watch—out of the corner of my eye—dark babies climbing trees.

I was sitting thinking how dull life was at the moment when a tall blond man in shirtsleeves came across to my table bringing his beer from the counter.

"Do you mind if I join you?" he asked.

He spoke with a slight Scandinavian accent. I didn't mind if he sat at my table, though all the others were unoccupied. Perhaps he's waiting for a ship, too, I thought, and feels as depressed as I do. The man suddenly spoke:

"I am a merchant seaman. You know if it is possible for me to join the Royal Navy in Freetown?"

I frowned at him. A forty-pounds-a-month Scandinavian seaman wanting to join the Navy?

"Why?" I asked suspiciously. "I mean, why should you want to do that?"

He laughed and I could see the gold stoppings in his teeth.

"Ah, well you may ask," he said, suddenly peering round furtively, then going on: "I am Norwegian, but married to British girl I have not seen for two years. So I jumped ship here in Freetown to-day."

He pronounced "jumped" as "yumped." I nodded, expecting more, and got it:

"This ship I was on, you see, never sail to England. Run all the time between here, Halifax, and Buenos Aires."

"Curious habit," I commented.

It sounded a very improbable run to me. The man shrugged.

"I have a friend on board and two hundred dollars in Canadian money. If I could get the dollars...."

"Why didn't you bring them with you?" I asked.

The man hesitated.

"Well, I did not intend to jump ship this morning, then when I have been ashore for an hour or two I get the idea of volunteering for your Royal Navy. I think they would send me to England for training. Yes?"

I shook my head. His mind seemed to be paved with crazy ideas.

"No," I replied. "They won't take you if you're a merchant seaman—that is, not here. If you could get to England you'd probably be all right, but you'd have to sign off your ship properly first."

He now shook *his* head, vigorously, like a wet dog.

"The captain would not hear of it," he said. "I try to sign off in Halifax and pick up a Britain bound tanker, but there was nothing doing."

It was a fishy story and I didn't like the smell of it at all. Merchant seamen were only obliged to sign six-monthly articles and there was nothing to prevent this man from leaving his ship at Halifax and waiting in the M.N. pool until he could get a ship to the U.K., that is, if he had put in six months' service on the merchantman in question.

"What ship are you on, mate?" the man asked suddenly.

The "mate" sounded forced, even for a foreigner. He might be a German, I thought, or a quisling working for the Germans. There was some spying done at Freetown, that was obvious; there was also some sabotage. Natives were bribed to swim out in the bay at night and stick limpet-mines on ships' rudders or propellers. Probably, I reflected, they were the natives who shouted God-Bless-King-George the loudest when they were plying their daytime bumboat trades.

I watched a fly hovering over a small pool of beer on the table.

"I'm not on a ship," I answered, "I'm drinking beer in a N.A.A.F.I."

I drained my glass.

"Have another?" I suggested.

He laughed and again showed the gold stoppings.

"Ya, sure," he said.

I stood up and walked over to the counter.

"Two tins of Brasso," I said to the server.

He promptly set about opening two cans of beer. I dropped my voice:

"Get the naval police here at once. The bloke sitting at that table might be a Jerry."

The server, to give him credit, never flickered an eyelash or looked up from what he was doing. I thought he hadn't heard.

"Got that?" I said in a low voice.

"That'll be one and six, Jack," he answered, and as he gave me my change added, "We always do our best to please the customers."

Then I knew he had heard. He disappeared from behind the counter and I guessed he had gone to phone. I went back to the table and poured the beers. The "seaman" became affable, gave me a cigarette, and as he was lighting it said:

"You want to earn some money, sailor, big money?"

"How big?" I asked.

"A hundred pounds. Two hundred, maybe."

"That depends," I answered, blowing out a cloud of smoke, "on how it's to be earned."

"Just by answering a few questions."

"About what?"

"Ships."

"Oh, ships," I said. "I don't know."

I must keep him talking till they get here, I thought.

"Just what nationality are you?" I asked.

He smiled a gold-stopped, toothy smile.

"I'm a neutral," he said softly. "It's more profitable."

He can't be a German, I thought, he's too stupid. Fancy offering me money before he knows whether I can answer his questions or not. He must be a stooge hired by an agent to do the dirty work of making contacts. I glanced towards the street, hoping to see a naval picket coming up it at the double. There were two natives pushing a cart full of light, bungalow furniture. Nobody else. My companion looked at me suspiciously.

"Are you expecting someone?" he demanded.

He looked dangerous, but for some reason I had no fear of him. I was only afraid of torpedoes nowadays.

"An oppo of mine said he might call in for a drink," I said casually. "But it's late. He won't come now."

"An 'oppo'?" he queried.

"A friend. Short for 'opposite number'," I explained.

The man relaxed.

"Ah, good," he said. "Then we can talk, but first I get you some more beer."

It would take a lot more of *that* beer to make me talk, I thought, as he stood up and went over to the counter. Then my attention was drawn to a blue R.N. van swinging round the corner. It pulled up with a quiet squeal outside the N.A.A.F.I. and out of it jumped six matelots with truncheons followed by an anvil-jawed petty officer. The P.O. had a revolver holster at his belt. Softly they came up the steps and into the bar. The P.O. looked across at me, the only one sitting at a table. I nodded towards the back of the Jerry stooge who was still busy buying what he thought was talking beer. As he turned round he found himself confronted by seven of the roughest looking specimens of naval life certainly I'd ever seen.

"Let's see your papers," the P.O. said.

The stooge was completely nonplussed.

"I—I haven't got them on me. They're in my coat. It's at my house," he said, looking murderously in my direction.

"Search him, then take him away," said the petty officer to his sailor-policemen.

There was a scuffle as they reached the street and the man tried to bolt. One of the matelots tripped him, another snapped a pair of handcuffs on him, then they bundled him into the Blue Maria and climbed in after him. The P.O. watched with satisfaction, then came over to me, notebook and pencil in hand.

"Name and number," he said.

"Henry Warren, A.B., D/JX 214634," I answered smartly.

The P.O. wrote it down.

"What you doin' ashore this time o' day anyhow?" he asked.

"I haven't any duties. Survivor. DEMS. Waiting for a ship to the U.K."

"All right. What's the story?"

I told him. There wasn't really much to tell, but he wrote it all down.

"Tried to bribe you, eh? We'll fix the bastard," he said grimly.

I almost felt sorry for the Jerry stooge—almost.

"I expect the civvy police'll want a statement from you," the P.O. added.

"Now?"

"No. In a day or two."

I went back to the Pomfret Cake. They were piping my name and number all over the ship through the loud-hailer system. I rushed to the drafting office.

"Where you bin?" bellowed the chief.

I started to tell him.

"Never mind," he cut in. "Signal from DEMS ashore. Immediate draft, s.s. *Calisto*. Gunlayer's gorn sick. Took queer all of a sudden, or somefink. Git yer bag and 'ammick, at the double."

"But chief, I haven't got a hammock. I only had one on loan and——" I began.

"I don't want to know abaht that. I allus sez, 'Git yer bag and 'ammick'. I been sayin' it for thirty years. I can't change now. Besides," he turned his attention to some papers on the desk, "I don't want to. Well, don't stand there. Git yer bag and 'ammick!"

The chief shook his nineteen stones at me. Did I say I was only afraid of torpedoes nowadays? I doubled away as fast as my legs could double me. Two hours later I was at sea, gunlayer of the s.s. *Calisto,* homeward bound!

IX

I WAS LUCKY not to have been held to give evidence against the Jerry hireling, a thing which would have delayed my draft. As it was the police would probably send to the *Pomfret Castle* for me in a day or two. Hard luck on them. Wild sea-horses wouldn't drag me back to Freetown now.

The s.s. *Calisto* was a meat boat returning from Sydney. One of her ports of call had been Pitcairn Island and most of the crew had souvenirs in the form of snuff-boxes (quite useless), walking sticks, and cigarette boxes, all made out of some dark wood which wasn't teak or any other hardwood I'd ever seen. The men said that a lot of the islanders had the same names as some of the Bounty's mutineers. There were Christians, Mills, Churchills, Browns, Burkitts, McCoys, Smiths, Williams, Martins, Skinners, and others—according to one member of the *Calisto's* crew who had no doubt refreshed the list with the aid of Nordhoff and Hall's book. However, I envied them their visit to this famous yet still unspoiled island. They had gone to Australia via the Panama Canal, so this was the last leg of their round-the-world voyage. I felt sorry for, yet grateful to the gunlayer who had been taken ashore with suspected appendicitis and had left me his splendid cabin on the upper-deck, aft.

There were two Maritime Regiment Lewis-gunners and two naval DEMS seaman-gunners who shared a big cabin next to mine. The rest of the gun crew was composed of merchant sea-men. The armament consisted of a 4-inch B.L. gun and a 12-pounder, both mounted right aft, two Lewis guns on the bridge and a .303 rifle in the gunlayer's cabin. I dined at the captain's table while the soldiers and seamen-gunners sat at another table, also in the saloon, with the apprentices and junior engineers. It was a pleasant company and the food was good.

The convoy consisted of seventeen ships, all fairly fast and all bound for the United Kingdom at a speed of twelve knots. The Frenchman, on which were Tom Potter and John Griffiths, was ahead of us on the port flank of the convoy. We were the last ship in this column. At times I wished I was on the Frog with my two friends, as we had been together for the past four months, but I counted myself lucky to have such a good ship as the *Calisto* under my feet. Perhaps we should meet again at some DEMS base, and Teddy Fox, too, I thought, not knowing that he was already dead. For an escort we had one destroyer, two frigates and a corvette. There was also a small rescue ship which brought up the rear and was chiefly for the purpose of picking up sur-vivors—though I believe she also carried Asdic—during or after an attack.

I drilled the guns' crews, as soon as we cleared the bar at Free-town, mainly to see what they were like, but also to impress the captain, for I'd noticed that he was something of a disciplinarian, though by no means a martinet. The *Calisto* was what is called, rather sentimentally, by seamen, a "happy ship." This was largely due to the captain's fair-mindedness. He kept a close watch on the stewards to see that there was no niggling or fiddling when it came to the crew's rations and the bos'n assured me that even he was not allowed to keep the money he got for selling old mooring ropes—a traditional habit of bos'n's who perhaps originated the saying, "Money for old rope"—but had to share it among the crowd. The bos'n wasn't annoyed about this, but seemed to be rather surprised and one might even say, uplifted—which rather surprised me as I'd never seen an uplifted bos'n before.

Captain Farquhar was not more than forty, tall, with greying hair and quick, blue eyes. Merchant Navy captains are in the happy position of being able to wear just what they like. One I knew later always wore plus-fours, golfing jacket and a flat cap at sea. Bowler hats are often in favour; because as mentioned be-fore they do not easily blow off. But the master of the *Calisto* was sophisticated in his appearance : he usually paced the scrubbed, flush deck or the bridge in smart grey or white flannels and blue yachting jacket—as if he owned the boat.

I took plenty of exercise with Jock, one of the Army gunners who was an amateur, middle-weight boxer and longed for sparring partners so much that he would make written statements promising not to hurt anybody—much—if they would volunteer to train with him. After extracting one of these promissory notes, for what it was worth, I became Jock's daily sparring partner, or chopping block. True to his written word he did not punch heavily at the face, but the blows he rained on my body left no doubt as to his punching ability. On the third day at sea I was covered with bruises and asked for a couple of days rest until the soreness wore off. Jock was very concerned and offered to pay me compensation—this was part of the "contract"—at the rate of one pint of beer per bruise, as soon as we reached port. I counted nineteen potential pints on my torso.

To give the previous gunlayer credit, his gun crews were in very good shape : quick, alert, and faultless in their drill. It only needed half an hour a day on each gun to keep them in trim. The Army gunners were trained in the use of the 4-inch and 12-pounder as well as their machine guns. There were five of us servicemen for full-time watchkeeping, then, and two merchant seamen, both stewards, who carried out their normal duties and were paid overtime for watchkeeping. The captain liked to have two gunners on watch at a time, both on the gun-deck aft, but as we were an odd number I asked if I might keep one watch alone. He agreed, which meant that we did two hours on and six off, right round the clock, an admirable arrangement. There was plenty of time for eating, sleeping, sunbathing, reading, gun-drilling and boxing, and that is how we lived for a week as the convoy steamed northwards through the tropical blue waters, with the flying fish racing beside us as if they too were hurrying home.

Greek love existed between the two stewards, Art and Chris, and was accepted by the crew, to whom they were known as Art and Craft, or Sodom and Gomorrah. They were a devoted pair and lived happily together in a cabin on the upper-deck, as they were in the gun crews, instead of a "glory hole"—as stewards' accommodation is called on merchant ships. Both were keen on jazz and had a good selection of records which they played on a portable gramophone. This they sometimes took with them on watch, set up on an ammunition locker, and jived to its music round and round the gun-platform. I had to stop this, not that I objected to their dancing together. It was very entertaining, but jitterbugging didn't make for good watchkeeping and they were being paid overtime for watchkeeping, after all.

Jock and the other Army gunner, a quiet Geordie, kept watch together, while Seaman-Gunner Greene, a grumbling Yorkshire lad and his opposite number, a fastidious Lancastrian who claimed to own three shoe shops in Manchester, kept another. I had the fourth watch in solitary splendour.

X

WE WERE off Maderia, about two hundred miles west of the island, when the first Focke-Wulf appeared. It encircled the convoy well out of range of any A.A. weapons either the merchantmen or any of their escorts carried. We closed up at the guns and stayed there all day, having food sent up to us from the galley, but the German aircraft never made an attack. It simply crawled through the cloudless sky, round, and round, and round us all afternoon. We were all stiff-necked and nerve-racked watching it. This was the idea of course: work us up into a state of nervous agitation then attack—by U-boats. I had heard of the new technique the Germans were using, but this was the first time I'd experienced it. At about five o'clock the Focke-Wulf was relieved by another, which flew away at dusk. We stayed at the guns all night, expecting a U-boat attack, sleeping—or trying to sleep—while one of us kept watch. The attack never came. At dawn a Focke-Wulf appeared and began its vigil until noon.

"Gone 'ome to get 'is flickin' dinner I suppose," commented Yorky Greene, as the Focke-Wulf streaked for the horizon and its relief took over.

I was sick with fear and trying not to show it before the other gunners. It wouldn't have mattered much if I had. Each of them had a personal fear-aura which enveloped them according to their individualities. Jock the boxer, for instance, cursed incessantly in an even thicker Glaswegian accent than he normally had; Art danced to some inner, rhythmic compulsions round and round the 12-pounder turret for hours on end—or so it seemed; Seaman-Gunner Greene loudly criticized, with bitter passion the Government, the war, the Navy, the Germans and the gods themselves for allowing them all to exist. No doubt I could have found some similar fear re-action, but I tried to bottle the temptation and look calm and efficient instead.

"You don't look very worried about all this, considering you've had the hammer twice," said Chris, on the second Focke-Wulf day.

If he'd listened attentively he'd have heard my teeth rattling. If anyone had dropped a spanner on the deck I'd have jumped over the side.

Action came as a relief three days after the first Focke-Wulf made its appearance, when we were about five hundred miles west of Cape Finisterre. Three aircraft were now encircling the convoy which made us think that an attack was imminent. The dark shapes of the planes reminded me of the vultures over the grammar school court in Freetown. Superstitiously, I now regarded the birds as omens, evil things of darkness. I did not realize, then, that the world is composed of images and reflections which, apart from their visual aspect, need have no bearing on one another. It is often we who impose our own unconsciously selected patterns on the universe.

On the afternoon of this third day out of the blue came two Hudsons of British Coastal Command. The vulturous Jerries fled for their French air bases with the Hudsons in pursuit. We cheered wildly as one of the Germans plunged flaming into the sea, caught in the cross-fire of both British planes. But our cheers died on the air as a spout of water rose from the side of a ship in the next column to ours, and we heard the muffled explosion of a torpedo.

The ship, a small cargo vessel of some three or four thousand tons, began to sag midships, her little back well and truly broken. Small figures, some carrying personal belongings, all in lifejackets, were leaping from the decks and swimming away from the stricken ship. Half-folded, her mast tops almost touching, and with men still on her decks, the tramp ship sank rapidly beneath the dazzling waves. The rescue ship was already picking up the first few swimming survivors.

"And that," remarked Jock, looking at his watch, "took two minutes fifteen seconds."

"Iron ore, that's what she was carrying," said Chris.

The words were no sooner spoken than a torpedo struck us under the stern, almost directly beneath the gun-platform. I recognized the familiar double bump as the tin-fish first struck then exploded. Immediately after this I had the impression of steel pressing on the soles of my feet, then I was shooting upwards with a great wall of water. There was a sudden shock as I hit the sea's surface, pains in my head and back, then darkness as I sank beneath the waves.

As I fought, kicking and struggling to the surface, one thing, a garbled line of verse, kept repeating itself in my head: Full Fathom Six. Full Fathom Six. Full Fathom Six. Full Fathom Six. Full Fathom Six. FULL FATHOM SIX! As I breached, the last phrase thundered out of my bursting ears, it seemed, and I gulped down lungfuls of salty, choking air and water. Whether "Full Fathom Six" was an indication of the depths I'd sounded I don't know. I very much doubt it. Thirty-six feet is not the depth you fall to accidentally with all that deep-sea pressure—though it certainly *seemed* a thirty-six foot climb to the surface. It was like struggling up a rock face with someone shoving from below.

I had an excruciating pain in the small of my back, as if I'd just performed one of those faulty high dives when your legs fold over and bend your spine too much. However, the slight injury didn't prevent me from swimming slowly. I had been wearing a rubber lifebelt, issued on the *Pomfret Castle*, and I now felt for the mouthpiece of this, intending to inflate it. To my horror I found the belt was missing! It must have been ripped off as I struck the water and I remembered now that the band which passed round the neck had been slightly torn. I'd intended to repair it. Good intentions! The waterproof pack containing my paybook and English pound note had been attached to the lifebelt, so it too was gone. I had worn the naval belt rather than the kapok M.N. type for comfort, as the weather in these latitudes was still too warm for the big padded waistcoat, during the daytime. Previous to the coming of the Focke-Wulf we had not worn any sort of lifejacket except during night watches.

In great fear at the realization that I had nothing but my own strength and buoyancy to keep me afloat, I struck out wildly in no particular direction—a stupid, normal, re-action. My back soon stopped me from continuing, however, and I floated for a while, exhausted by fear and wasted effort. There was a slight swell so that when I was lifted on the crest of a wave I could see the occasional outlines of ships of the now scattered convoy, but I could distinguish none of them, nor could I see any of the *Calisto's* crew in the water. I could hear several deep explosions which seemed to come from underneath me, and assumed that these were depth-charges, not really underneath me, of course. A stronger feeling of dread came over me, now that I knew I was alone. At least there had been plenty of society in the last shipwreck—too much in fact. I wondered how long I could keep afloat and whether the rescue ship would come looking for *Calisto* survivors. Somewhere I'd read of an idea to tread water for an indefinite period by taking in a shallow breath of air, allowing oneself to sink in a vertical position just below the surface of the water, floating up to the top again, taking in air and repeating the process. I tried to do it but panicked as soon as I went under, reminded of my first upward struggle, and thinking that if I were under the surface at the instant a lookout glanced in my direction I should not be seen. I began instead to swim a slow breast-stroke. This wasn't difficult as I was only wearing shorts, my shoes having departed with the lifebelt, but soon an additional fear gripped me as the sound of depth-charges exploding came nearer. I could feel the shock-waves on my body and short jars in my spine as if an electric current were passing intermittently through it, every time a charge exploded. For what seemed hours I swam on and on, slowly, listening to and *feeling* the charges, wondering when one was going to burst so close that I'd be slit up the middle and gutted like the dead fish I'd seen on the surface when I'd shot up the mine, a long time ago. A charge burst so close that I felt as if I'd been lifted a few feet out of the water and dropped back again, but I hadn't really left it. The next one, I thought, will get me. In a few minutes I'll be lying face upwards, gutted like a dead fish. Nothing mattered now. I waited, resigned to this ignoble finish. But no charge exploded and I thought I saw the form of a ship, surprisingly close. I raised an arm out of the water with difficulty. . . .

XI

SOME TIME later I was distantly aware of being hauled up a scramble-net by several strong pairs of hands, then somebody was pouring a tot of rum between my lips as I lay on the deck of what turned out to be our escort destroyer. The rum had the usual volcanic effect of bringing me to an immediate state of burning, vomiting alertness.

Having rid my stomach of salt water I felt better, and one of the matelots who had helped to haul me aboard said that I'd been muttering something about "fathoms" all the time.

"Full Fathom Six?" I suggested.

"Yeh, that was it," he answered. "What's it all about?"

I shook my head. Didn't know.

"Thanks for pulling me out," I said.

"Aw, that's all right, mate. Have a burn."

He gave me a cigarette and lit it. It tasted extra strong, but good, very good. God bless the sea-going Navy, I thought, as I puffed contentedly at the outsize ship's Woodbine. The destroyer had not stopped to pick me up but had simply slowed down to about five knots and scooped me out of the water in passing, as it were, then continued on her submarine hunt. I had only actually been in the water an hour and a half, though it had seemed four hours at least.

Now the destroyer raced about, throbbing and vibrating, at thirty knots. She lobbed depth-charges from her sides and rolled them at intervals every time a flag was held up by a signalman on the bridge, over the stern. Gun's crews were closed up, tense and strange in their anti-flash helmets and gloves, (which we in the DEMS never bothered to wear) while ammunition-supply and fire parties stood by.

A doctor and sick berth attendant came along to where I was

now sitting with my back to the galley and my knees drawn up to my chin.

"Come on," said the S.B.A., "we're going to take you to the Bay."

"Can't I stay here?" I asked the doctor. "I'm all right."

I stood up and he looked at me. My back still hurt a bit and my legs felt weak. It was like having a touch of 'flu.

"Want to see the fun, eh?" the Quack grinned.

"Well, sir, I was rather enjoying the sensation of hunting as a change from being hunted," I admitted, "that was the third ship I've lost."

"All right, then," the doctor answered, "but report to me later and I'll have a look at you. No pains anywhere have you?"

I shook my head.

"Nothing much."

After they had gone I slumped down on the deck feeling weak but exhilarated by the speed and excitement of life on this, to me, utterly different kind of ship. The P.O. cook handed me a pint of hot tea which I gulped down, burning my lips, mouth and throat, but ridding myself of the taste of salt and rum, to some extent.

Dreamily I wondered what had become of the *Calisto's* crew. Someone had said she'd been hit twice and had sunk quickly. This was quite likely as there was little buoyancy in her cargo of frozen meat, and if she had been hit twice no wonder I hadn't seen her. She must have taken most of the crew with her, I thought. No boats could have got away. As far as I knew I was the *Calisto's* only survivor, though it turned out afterwards that half a dozen members of the crew, including Jock the boxer, Sea-man-Gunner Greene, the third officer, chief steward and one A.B. were picked up. All had been wearing kapok jackets, Jock and Greene had been sucked down a little way but managed to sur-face, while the other three and, I think, an engineer were blown clear when the second torpedo struck, and later picked up, dazed, but unhurt.

Four ships had been sunk all told and it was thought that the attack had been carried out by three submarines, two of which had sheered off, but the third, it was believed, was somewhere in the vicinity, lying low. The convoy and other escorts were re-forming and pressing northwards with the air cover of the Hud-sons, while we, the fastest and most efficient anti-submarine ship, stayed behind to search for the third U-boat.

It seemed as though we had lost her; no depth-charges were released, though the men stood by them. The gunners relaxed; food and buckets of tea were taken up to the turrets, the ammo-

supply and fire-parties lit furtive dog-ends and puffed quietly
in corners. The ship's engines slowed, the vibration ceased, and
I began to feel disappointed and depressed. It was like being on
a merchantman again. Finally the engines stopped altogether.
Alarmed, I got up and holding on to a lifeline worked my way
towards the torpedo tubes where a party of torpedomen with
their chief, the torpedo gunner's mate, were standing by.

"What's wrong?" I asked them. "Why have we stopped?"

The T.G.M. turned round.

"Whatsat? Oh, just so's he thinks we've gone away. P'raps,"
he said, adding the last word thoughtfully.

It seemed a dangerous game, leaving oneself a sitting duck,
hoping that the U-boat might think we'd gone away. Suppose
he too had stopped his engines and was now sitting at periscope
depth peeping at us, with a kipper up the spout ready to let fly
at us? Just at that moment a cold wind swept across the destroyer's deck and I shuddered. The T.G.M. turned to one of the torpedomen:

"You, Spare Number, nip below and get some warm gear for
Lofty here. Can't you see the poor naked man's shivering? Want
him to catch his death?"

The sailor doubled away and came back with a thick jersey, a
pair of white shorts, gym shoes and a puff-up lifebelt. I thanked
him and put them on, first removing and wringing out my old
wet shorts and later leaving them in the galley to dry. Now I felt
better, warm and safe. The pain in my back had eased considerably so I concluded that it was only muscular. It was a relief in
itself to know this. Now all I wanted was something to do, so I
teamed up with the ammo-supply party who were standing by
near A gun turret. Suddenly the engines roared and the ship came
alive again. A ping! The buzz went round the ship like an electric
current. The Asdic was on to something again and away we
raced, heaving round in a half-circle and stepping up the speed,
fifteen knots, seventeen, twenty, twenty three, twenty seven,
thirty! We plunged into the wind and waves, flinging up huge
fans of spray on either side of the bows. We dropped a pattern
of depth-charges and felt slight lifts as the sea mushroomed upwards in several places in our wake.

"All right, mate?" one of the O.D.'s of the ammo-supply party
said, nudging me, and offering a cigarette.

"All right, mate," I answered, taking it.

This was the sort of Navy to be in, I thought, feeling the com-
radeship and watching the sailors' grinning, excited faces as we
rushed along with the wind roaring in our ears. We slowed,
turned and came back over the same area, patterning the water

as before. Just as the last two charges of this run had rolled over the stern, a lookout shouted from the bridge :

"Submarine surfacing, sir!"

We all looked astern. Already part of the conning tower was visible as the U-boat rose slowly, bows uppermost, gun pointing upwards like an H.A. weapon.

"Collision stations !"

The order came clearly and calmly over the loud-hailer, then : "Stand by to ram."

We slowed, turned, and pointed our bows towards the submarine which now wallowed on the surface. Some Germans were trying to train their gun in our direction, others were already pouring out of the conning tower and fore-hatch, holding their hands high above their heads, then jumping off the casing into the sea. We raced towards the submarine at thirty knots, like an angry bull with a wounded matador in front of him. There would be no quarter till the thing was destroyed. The distance closed : four hundred yards, three hundred, two hundred . . . matelots scampered about with lashed hammocks to use as stop-gaps if we holed ourselves. Everybody had moved to positions abaft the bridge and were bracing themselves for the crash. The ship's speed fell to twenty-five, to twenty, to fifteen knots. I hung onto a lifeline and peered cautiously over the side, towards our bows. I was just in time to see the insignia on the U-boat's conning tower before the destroyer cleft her in two, flinging me and several others of the ammo-gang flat on our faces. It was the Ace of Spades.

I could only think that what might have caused this possible improbability was the fact that the Ace of Spades, after a successful patrol off the West Coast, had been returning to her base when she was ordered to rendezvous with the two other U-boats which had been sent to attack the convoy. Reports from one or two of the sullen, oil-soaked survivors partly confirmed this, though not much information was gained from them. They numbered only twelve and no officers were among them. I felt a slight pang when I heard that their commander had perished. He hadn't treated us badly after sinking the Astrid, but, as he himself had said : "In the classic phrase, war is war." He must have sunk a hundred thousand tons of our shipping and killed dozens of merchant seamen. The high seas were well rid of him.

The U-boat survivors were passed lashed hammocks and made to stuff them into holes in our now leaky bows. Watertight doors were then closed and clamped tightly on the packed hammocks— not the Germans—as we turned and headed for the convoy, at twenty-five knots.

"Re-fit in Birkenhead now. Bags o' leave. Yippee !" crowed a Scouse A.B. on the mess-deck that evening.

He didn't care about not having a hammock to sleep in. Nor did anyone else seem to mind. There was so little sleeping done on a destroyer anyway.

XII

A WEEK LATER I stepped ashore in Liverpool. It was late April and still rather chilly, especially after the tropics. A light rain fell on the docks, now in a dreadful state after several heavy bombings. Even the overhead railway—the dockers' umbrella, as it was sometimes called—was only functioning between certain halts, a bomb having shattered it by the northernmost docks. I gazed up at the eagles on the Royal Liver Buildings, wondering what sort of reception I should get at the DEMS office there when I turned up in jersey and trousers (not shorts, thankfully) gym shoes and an old watchcoat I'd borrowed from the destroyer —and no paybook ! I had said good-bye to the destroyer-men, envying them their comparative security and good companionship. The DEMS seemed a lonely life where you were continually being separated from the few friends you made, as you went along from one damned merchant packet to another. I had never, I reflected, been with any other gunner for more than three or four months. Wherever I'd gone I had been a stranger, asked who I was, what I was, why I was dressed like this, or like that.

But I need not have worried about my reception at the Liver Buildings. DEMS Liverpool were used to half-clad gunners trailing into their offices at all hours of the day, feeling both heroic and sorry for themselves at the same time. They were quite blasé about the whole affair. I saw the commander and spun my yarn.

"So you caught it twice, this time ?" he said, as if I'd had some mild disease.

"Yes, sir," I answered, feeling rather guilty.

"Well, never mind. At least you had the satisfaction of seeing one of theirs go to the bottom," the commander said heartily.

Satisfaction ? I wondered if this was the right word. War is war —the classic phrase. Yes, satisfaction, I supposed, and nodded.

"Then we'll see about leave for you. I think about three weeks, don't you, Chief ?" the commander turned to the inevitable bodyguard-witness inquiringly.

The chief agreed.

It should have been four weeks. A survivor from *one* lost ship got two, but I couldn't argue with a commander.

The paymaster, a pale, efficient young man, R.N.V.R., probably an accountant in some former life, didn't fuss much about my not having a paybook. He gave me five pounds and promised to forward the balance—if any—to my leave address. I was to go across to Birkenhead, get some new gear and, having dressed in some of it, leave the bulk of the stuff at the new DEMS billet a tram-ride out of town. Then I could go on leave.

"But wait a moment," the paybob stopped me just as I was about to go, "I've been waiting for you to show up. Now, where was that signal. Ah, here it is."

He had plucked a sheaf of papers from a file and riffled through them while he had been talking.

"Warren, H., D/Jx 214634. That is you, isn't it?" he said, peering over the top of his glasses.

I said it was.

"You took part in the salvage of a motor vessel, the *Marseillaise,* just over a year ago?"

I said yes again, hopefully this time. The paybob sat back in his chair, took off his glasses and looked as if he'd eaten something disagreeable for lunch.

"I'm sorry to disappoint you," he said, "but no salvage money was paid."

"Oh," I said flatly.

He leaned forward, put his elbows on the desk and made a cage with his thin, white fingers.

"You see," he explained, "it was an Admiralty-chartered vessel and the cargo, crude oil as you know, belonged to them."

The cage of fingers collapsed expressively. He went on:

"However, Their Lordships did consent to make an *ex gratia* payment to the captain, his officers and crew, and to the handful of volunteers who helped to bring the ship to port—of which you yourself were one."

"Ah," I murmured.

Ex gratia—"out of charity." Still, it was money.

The paymaster leaned back and looked ill again.

"But unfortunately Their Lordships do not make *ex gratia* payments to naval ratings and you, of course, are a naval rating," he said.

Of course. Airily he continued:

"It didn't amount to very big shares, a few thousand pounds for the captain, a few hundreds each for the seamen. . . ."

He maundered on:

". . . of little consequence . . . we of the Royal Navy . . . cannot expect such considerations . . . do not *want* such rewards. . . ."

I knew what I wanted. I wanted to get out of this man's pale presence before I took him and shook the spectacles off his nose!

"May I go now, sir?" I said, cutting into his arm-chair patriotic monologue.

"What? Oh, yes, very well. You've got everything? Good. Next," he called to the Wren assisting him to send in the next for payment.

I went to Birkenhead, got my kit, returned to Liverpool and the DEMS billet with it. I didn't like the look of the billet. It was too big and well-organized. There were too many chiefs and P.O.'s around the place, besides a number of newly-made leading seamen. No, the DEMS was getting too efficient. I must look for some different branch, but later; leave first.

In the early evening I was in the train heading south for home. The sun was still shining, the rain had stopped. The trees and fields, though few at first, were green, English green. I marvelled at their intense colours after the dark hues of Africa. It was nearly the end of another long war-time journey, and it would not be the last. Where to next? I did not know, or care, for the moment. As it grew dark in the compartment I fell asleep.

To the Reader

If you would like to be advised
of our new books as and when
published, please send us a card
giving your name and address,
and this will ensure that you receive these particulars regularly

ROBERT HALE LIMITED
63 Old Brompton Rd · London SW7